# HELP!

## THE GRANDCHILDREN ARE COMING

MIKE HASKINS & CLIVE WHICHELOW

ILLUSTRATIONS BY IAN BAKER

summersdale

HELP! THE GRANDCHILDREN ARE COMING

An Hachette UK Company
www.hachette.co.uk

Summersdale Publishers Ltd
Part of Octopus Publishing Group Limited
Carmelite House
50 Victoria Embankment
LONDON
EC4Y 0DZ
UK

www.summersdale.com

Printed and bound in the Czech Republic

ISBN: 978-1-78685-792-7

Substantial discounts on bulk quantities of Summersdale books are available to corporations, professional associations and other organisations. For details contact general enquiries: telephone: +44 (0) 1243 771107 or email: enquiries@summersdale.com.

To ...........................

From .........................

# CONTENTS

It's one of the few phrases in the English language guaranteed to fill you with both delight and dread – the grandchildren are coming!

Of course you love to see them, but what do you do with them for the next few hours – or even days?

And it's all different from when your kids were kids. These days the grandchildren might have their own mobile phones, electronic tablet thingies, iPods, virtual reality headsets, possibly even rocket-launchers and jetpacks too, but the parents will most likely not want their kids playing with any of those while they're at their grandparents', thank you very much. No, you have to amuse them.

But how?

Well, the funny thing is, despite all the electronic gizmos, gadgets and thingummyjigs mentioned above, there are certain things that will keep kids amused which may have kept you amused back in the day.

Jokes (the sillier the better), puzzles, games, fascinating facts, riddles, magic tricks...

But can you remember any of them? You can vaguely recall your granddad pulling sweets out from behind his ear, but how on earth did he do it? You seem to remember a trick involving a coin and two matchsticks (or was it three?) but you're blowed if you can remember how it went. Then there were the jokes. 'Knock, knock! Who's there? I can't remember.' isn't going to cut any mustard with your darling grandchildren, is it?

Which is why we've devised this book. When the grandchildren turn up you will no longer be frozen with fear, delirious with ditherment or frankly flummoxed with what to do next to keep them amused.

You will be able to choose from games old and new, tricks that even you won't be able to mess up, jokes that will make you the first sit-down stand-up comedian and a host of other delights to make the hours fly by until their parents finally come to collect them.

Then there will be cries of 'We don't want to go home, we're having fun'. At this point you have to quickly bar the exit so the parents don't see this as a cue to disappear for another few hours while you do some more unpaid babysitting for them.

However, you will be able to promise the grandkids lots more fun next time as you raid the pages of this book for things to keep them amused and you sane.

Have fun!

# HOW TO USE THIS BOOK

The book has been divided into sections so that you can choose from games, tricks, jokes, etc. Within those sections are subsections, so under 'games' you will also find 'games to play on public transport'. These will hopefully be more socially acceptable than games devised by the children themselves such as throwing ice creams on the heads of passers-by.

There are games that they can play in the car and games that involve complete silence (ah, bliss!).

There are games that involve using stuff destined for the bin, so that if you play your cards right you can get them sorting out your rubbish for recycling under the guise of having fun.

Then there are the jokes. They are all family-friendly so will avoid the embarrassment of Granddad inadvertently repeating a highly unsuitable one that he heard at the pub last night.

You'll be able to choose from groanworthy puns, knock-knock jokes and question-and-answer jokes (which are good for checking that the child you are speaking to is still awake).

The tricks should be foolproof, perhaps even grandparentproof, though we have decided to err on the side of caution and not include the one where Granddad saws Grandma in half. Let's leave that for volume two. One step at a time, eh?

And riddles. Do kids want to hear riddles in the twenty-first century? Well, within 30 seconds of hearing a good riddle a kid'll try that riddle on somebody else, guaranteed.

If none of the above does the trick, you've got shaggy dog stories, secret codes, fascinating facts…

There should be enough here to keep grandparents and grandchildren from driving each other crazy for hours.

Knock, knock. Who's there? The grandchildren. Bring it on!

# THE ADVANTAGES OF BEING A GRANDPARENT

Let's face it, there have to be some advantages to being older, don't there? Apart from a lifetime of acquired wisdom, experience and the get-out clause of a dodgy knee when any heavy lifting needs to be done, you can be an honorary parent.

It's a bit like those people who become honorary deans of colleges and don't have to do much apart from turn up on speech day and get treated like royalty.

A grandparent doesn't have to do any of the boring stuff with kids like getting them to wash behind their ears or tidy their rooms; or the stuff they'll hate you for, like taking them to the dentist or forcing them to wear their school uniform.

A grandparent just gets to do the fun stuff like going to the zoo, playing on the swings, eating ice creams, watching all those great kids' films you haven't seen for years…

And by and large you can choose the hours – unlike the poor old 24/7 parents.

Yes, as a grandparent you can famously give them back at the end of the day! Although do make sure you give them back to the correct people. Don't just hand them back to anyone you can find to get them off your hands.

At the end of the day, your grandchildren are ultimately their parents' responsibility. You can sit back and relax because you cannot be held legally responsible for anything your grandchildren may do wrong. Although of course you may instead be held legally responsible for things that one or other of their parents do.

Looking after your grandchildren will help you feel young again by reminding you of the days when you had small children of your own – but luckily this time you've got the job on a part-time basis.

And as a grandparent you can have fun with the grandchildren and behave in an equally childlike way with them. What's the point of having a second childhood if you can't enjoy it?!

# GAMES TO PLAY WITH THE KIDS

Of course you could dust off that old game of Snakes and Ladders that has been languishing in the attic for the past 30 years, or try your luck with Monopoly or one of your other rainy-day standbys, but why not be a bit more inventive?

For a start, you've got all the games you grew up with – such as Hide and Seek, Hunt the Thimble, Squeak Piggy Squeak, Charades and all the rest – plus the pencil and paper games such as Hangman (a bit politically incorrect these days – should it be Hangperson?). And you could come up with your own variations.

The variations, though, have to be carefully thought through. It's probably not a good idea to get the kids to close their eyes and count to a thousand while you nip down the pub for a cheeky half.

If you're really feeling adventurous you could go out in the street with a piece of chalk and teach them the rudiments of Hopscotch. Although it may be best to avoid some of the more antisocial games you used to play, like Knock Down Ginger or British Bulldog.

There are even some games that you can play without expending any energy whatsoever, or games that involve keeping very quiet – very grandparenty!

And some of these games will be educational. When you play Twenty Questions and ask 'Animal, vegetable or mineral?' you may have to explain what a mineral is. You may even have to explain what a vegetable is to some of today's kids!

You can play games with some of the old rubbish, er, recyclables, around the house. Who knew that a loo roll tube could be so adaptable? The kids will also be fascinated to find out that a telephone made with two old tin cans and a piece of thread does not need recharging or a 12-month contract. True, they may not be able to check their Facebook page on it, but that should be seen as an advantage!

# CLASSIC GAMES

## Hunt the Thimble

Before you start this game, it is good to have a thimble ready; otherwise, when the grandchildren arrive, you will be playing a game of Hunt the Thimble before you can start playing Hunt the Thimble, if you see what we mean. Children can get very fractious very quickly, so have your thimble ready!

Rules: get the children to look away or go into another room while you hide the thimble, then get them to find it! Perhaps have a small prize for the winner, or let them be the next to hide it.

What could be simpler? But it will keep them occupied for precious minutes while you get your breath back from whatever the previous activity was. And, of course, remember not to hide your thimble behind any of your most precious, highly fragile ornaments!

## Hide and Seek

The rules of this game hardly need explaining, but it's a perennial favourite and if the kids don't want to be found they have to remain very, very quiet. Crafty grandparents therefore will not find the children too readily and hence enjoy another few minutes of blissful peace!

## Twenty Questions

The beauty of this game is that it can be as simple or as difficult as you want it to be, depending on the age or ability of the grandchildren.

Rules: you think of something or someone and the children have to guess what or who it is by asking questions to which you can only reply 'Yes' or 'No'. They are only allowed a maximum of 20 questions and perhaps a small prize can be given to the person who gets the answer with the fewest guesses.

Some versions of this game begin by asking whether the thing in question is animal, vegetable or mineral, but as mentioned earlier this might confuse things a bit!

## Charades

Many grandparents will remember the TV version of this called *Give Us a Clue*.

Rules: if you have more than one grandchild, you can act as referee and get them to compete against one another. Slip a piece of paper with the title of a film, book, TV show or song (that they will have heard of!) to one grandchild and get them to act it out in a mime for the other(s) to guess. You may have to go first with a very easy mime to show how the game works. And if you have just one grandchild, it's going to be you against them! And they will have to think of their own titles to mime!

Harder than it sounds, and probably not suitable for very young (or very old!) players.

## Blind Man's Buff

Rules: one person is blindfolded and spun round in the middle of the room so they lose their orientation. The children should be advised not to spin Grandma or Granddad around too vigorously, especially if they haven't taken their pills yet. The other people then hide and the 'blind man' (probably a politically incorrect term these days!) has to find them. Once they find someone, it is that person's turn to be blindfolded.

Note: grandparents can legitimately excuse themselves from being blindfolded by saying that someone has to keep an eye on everyone else to make sure they're not cheating!

## Squeak Piggy Squeak

Rules: someone is blindfolded and given a cushion while everyone else sits themselves around the room. The blindfoldee then gropes around to find somebody's lap to sit on with the cushion. They then say 'Squeak piggy squeak!' and the person has to do their best pig impression (some may find this comes more naturally than others). The blindfoldee has to identify that person by their squeak. If wrong, they try again.

## I Spy

This is another game that probably requires little explanation, but grandparents may have to bear in mind the literacy levels of the kids. When a four-year-old says 'I spy with my little eye something beginning with "cuh"' that could be a K or a C. There's also a chance that the object the child has in mind is not even actually in the room at the time! Cat? But we haven't got a cat. Oh, you saw one on the way here… OK, fair enough.

# CLASSIC GAMES YOU SHOULDN'T TRY

At some point in the proceedings the children will no doubt have some suggestions of their own about what games to play next. Don't listen to them! Given a choice, children will often think of games that involve fighting, screaming, getting dirty and generally ruining the peaceful ambience of your lovely home. The following are some of the games that should be on your mental checklist of no-nos. If questioned on why not, you can claim that it is against local health and safety laws and maybe even have a bogus, official-looking banning order in a frame above your mantelpiece.

## British Bulldog

This is usually an outdoor game and although the kids might suggest it in anticipation of being given licence to charge around your living room causing mayhem and possible breakages – of bones and ornaments – it is highly inadvisable. How exactly would you explain it on your insurance claim form?

## Sardines

While it might be fine for the kids to squeeze themselves into tightly confined spaces, they will inevitably want you to join in. The only tightly confined space a person of your vintage should be attempting to squeeze into these days is your own trousers.

## Postman's Knock

It's hard enough getting them to give you a peck on the cheek at going home time, so an entire game based on kissing is a no-no.

## Murder in the Dark

Any game that is played in pitch darkness has obvious risks and pitfalls for anything breakable – you don't want your nick-nacks knocked, do you? Let alone the even more delicate objects in your house, such as yourself or your beloved grandkids.

## Apple Bobbing

Sloshing water, the dangers of wobbly teeth staying in the apple – it's all too horrible to contemplate, even if it is Hallow-flipping-een!

# GAMES INVOLVING NO EXPENSE OF ENERGY ON YOUR PART, BUT PLENTY ON THE PART OF THE KIDS

These games are the best of the lot. You get to sit or stand around giving instructions, while the kids are dashing hither and thither at your command and wearing themselves out so they're a bit more manageable later. Just don't let the power go to your head.

## What's the Time, Mr Wolf?

It's time for Grandma and Granddad to have a bit of a rest.

Rules: 'Mr Wolf' faces the wall while the children line up across the other side of the room. When they ask 'What's the time, Mr Wolf?' he replies 'One o'clock', 'Two o'clock' or whatever and the children walk towards him with the corresponding number of steps. At any time he feels like it Mr Wolf can reply 'It's dinner time!' and whip round with a blood-curdling growl and try to catch one of the kids. Mrs Wolf gets the best deal of the lot and sits the whole thing out.

## Treasure Hunt

Before the kids arrive you hide things around the room – coins, sweets, etc. They then have to find the treasure and you can give clues by saying 'You're getting warmer!' or 'You're getting colder!' You can also use the 'You're getting colder' line when they are getting dangerously close to one of your breakable prized heirlooms or the cat's tail.

## Simon Says

Suitable for all ages and even the grandparents are not guaranteed to win!

One person stands in front of the others and gives instructions such as 'Raise your right hand', 'Stand on one leg', etc. If the instruction is preceded by the words 'Simon says' then everyone has to follow it. If someone follows an instruction without these magic words, they're out!

Grandma will possibly have the unique pleasure of Granddad following her instructions for once.

# GAMES WHICH SECRETLY INVOLVE GETTING THE KIDS TO TIDY UP OR DO ODD JOBS ROUND THE HOUSE

## Who Can Find...?

After any session of cutting up paper to make joined-up paper people or pencil and paper games, there will inevitably be bits of paper all over the place. So you issue a challenge: 'Who can find the most pieces of paper? There's a special prize for the winner! Go!'

Children are a mercenary lot and if there's a bar of chocolate or a few bob in it they'll work like Trojans. Just beware that if you have a very intelligent child they will realise that by tearing the paper into even smaller pieces they will end up with the most and probably make even more mess in the process.

## Where Are Granny's Glasses?

The kids will imagine this is a game that Granddad has specially devised to amuse them and then to reward the winner with a special prize. Little do they know that Granddad himself has to play this game at least three or four times a day due to Granny's forgetfulness. There is a similar game that can be played for the amusement of all called Where are Granddad's Car Keys? There are many other variations of this perennial favourite.

## The Magic Treasure Detector

'Somewhere in this room,' you tell them, 'is some treasure. Some lovely, shiny, invisible coins that you can only find by using this magic treasure detector. Yes, it does look a bit like a Hoover, doesn't it? But it's not – it's my magic treasure detector!'

After they have finished hoovering your front room to the required standard you can then sneakily drop a couple of coins on the floor when they're not looking and say, 'Look! My magic treasure detector has found some money!' It'll be the cheapest home help you'll ever get.

## GAMES YOU CAN PLAY WHILE BOTH YOU AND THE KIDS SIT PERFECTLY STILL

### I Packed My Bag...

Simple, straightforward and involves no exertion whatsoever – hooray!

Rules: the first person says 'I packed my bag and in it I put...' then names an object such as a toothbrush or a comb, or anything they like really. The second person then repeats what the first person has said and adds their own item. This continues in turn around the assembled group until one of them makes a mistake or can't remember an item, at which point they are out. The last person remaining is the winner.

### Kim's Game

All old scouts and guides will remember this and possibly know that it was named after Rudyard Kipling's boy hero Kim, who was trained to be a spy.

Rules: one grandparent (probably the one with the worst memory) puts a dozen or so objects on a tray and covers it with a tea towel. They then whip the towel away for one minute while everyone tries to memorise all the objects. They then have to write down as many as they can remember and the winner is the one with the most.

## Chinese Whispers

The title is in all probability politically incorrect these days and there is probably no good reason why these whispers should be oriental but hey, it's been around forever and it's fun!

Rules: the players form a line and the person at one end whispers a message to the person next to them, who then whispers it to the next in line and so on until it gets to the end and the last person announces the message. At this point it is likely that the message has altered considerably from the original one, much to everyone's amusement (we hope!). Also, there are no winners and no losers, so therefore no arguments!

# GAMES THAT INVOLVE MAKING NO NOISE WHATSOEVER

Of course this 'no noise' element will depend entirely on whether people can refrain from crying because they've lost, accusing other people of cheating or kicking the wall in frustration – but then we expect you grandparents to set a good example!

## Stone, Paper, Scissors

Or Rock, Paper, Scissors if you must follow our American cousins. Do we need to explain the rules? Of course not. If you have never played this you have not had a proper childhood. Although it is often used as an elimination game for choosing someone to do something, it can be happily played as a game in its own right. And it's serious stuff. In 2005, auction house Christie's won the right to auction off £10-million-worth of art by winning this game against Sotheby's!

## Who Can Stay Quiet the Longest?

The lure of a prize will encourage even the noisiest of children to at least have a go at this self-explanatory game. The world record for a child staying quiet for the longest is rumoured to be approaching five seconds.

## Keep the Balloon Up

In theory, this game is for the toddlers, but even you grandparents won't be immune to the simple delights of trying to keep a balloon in the air for as long as possible, especially as it can be played sitting down.

Rules: there is only one rule – the balloon must not touch the floor. Otherwise you can kick it, punch it, head it, even blow it if you must. You can use your elbows, walking stick, a broom handle, anything you like. It's only a matter of time before it's an Olympic sport.

## Card Houses

This game involves such a level of hand–eye coordination and manual dexterity as to probably exclude those grandparents who can't find their glasses!

Rules: each child takes playing cards from a pile in the middle of the table and attempts to build the highest card house. Traditionally, the simplest one involves leaning two cards against each other in an 'A' formation, then making a second 'A' formation right beside the first for a bit of ballast before laying a single card across the top of the two 'A's. Continue adding further 'A' formations with single cards laid from the point of each 'A' to the next to make the first 'storey' of the house. You can then start the delicate work of adding further storeys on top, all built in similar fashion.

The person who can build the highest house within a certain time is the winner.

## Making Paper People

You will remember this one from your own childhood. Fold some paper into a bunched-up concertina shape and cut out half a person. When you open up the concertina you will have a string of people holding hands – or possibly a piece of paper with holes in it and a pile of confetti on the floor. Competitive grandparents may wish to progress to cutting out dinosaur shapes, or orangutans or things even more exotic.

## Statues

Sneaky grandparents can stretch this game out for as long as they like and have a bit of well-earned peace and quiet. With a bit of luck, you'll also wear the children out while you sit down and have a cup of tea.

Rules: get the children to walk around the room, then on a pre-arranged signal – e.g. you tapping the table or clicking your fingers – they have to stop, stay dead still and not move again until you give the signal. Anyone who doesn't stop on the command or starts moving again before the next command is out. The last remaining person is the winner.

## Pick-Up Sticks

The rapt concentration needed for this game should ensure it's played mainly in silence, assuming Grandma and Granddad can refrain from exclaiming 'Oh botheration!' or similar when it all goes wrong.

Rules: drop a pile of sticks in the middle of the table. You could use matchsticks, wooden kitchen skewers, chopsticks or anything else sticklike. The first person attempts to remove one at a time without disturbing any of the others. If they free one, they can continue; if not, the next person tries. The person with the most sticks at the end is the winner.

# GAMES USING A PEN AND PAPER

**Before there were computers and iPads and games consoles, we used to amuse ourselves with games that needed no more advanced technical equipment than a pen or pencil and a piece of paper. If you were adventurous you might use different coloured pens and pencils. And these games were just as exciting as today's electronic offerings! OK, good luck trying to persuade the grandchildren on that one! However, for a nice quiet few minutes of concentration and inter-generational competition, why not try introducing your grandchildren to one or two of the following games?**

## Noughts and Crosses

First draw a grid with three squares across and three squares down. Next choose which player will be 'noughts' and which 'crosses'. Actually, you probably don't need a detailed account of the full official rules and regulations of Noughts and Crosses, do you? It's a very simple game played by very bored people the world over. But it does provide some entertainment particularly if you instruct your grandchildren on how to avoid ever losing. In order to do this, you have to be the player who goes first and you have to begin by putting your 'X' or '0' in one of the corners!

## Dots and Boxes

Lay out a grid made up of dots as big or small as you like. Each player then takes turns to draw a line joining two adjacent dots either vertically or horizontally anywhere on the grid. If a player completes a square of four adjacent dots he/she wins this square and can proudly write their initial inside. This also wins them an extra go. Ultimately the player with his/her initial in most completed squares is the winner. Once again, you probably knew all that already didn't you! But it lasts slightly longer and involves a smidgen more brain power and excitement than Noughts and Crosses!

## Hangman

Yet again, it's one that we all know! One person thinks of a word or name and sets out a series of dashes for each of its letters. The other player suggests letters of the alphabet. If the letter occurs in the mystery word it is entered in the correct position, but if it doesn't, one element of the hangman's gallows is filled in. This continues until the mystery world is correctly identified, or the grizzly hangman's gallows is completed!

## Battleships

For this you'll need two pieces of paper (or one piece of paper torn into two if you're on a budget). Now draw an identical grid of squares on each. Maybe you'll go for ten squares down and ten across again. Or maybe you'd like your game to last the rest of the evening, in which case try grids with several hundred squares across and down!

Label each row of each grid going down a, b, c, d, etc. and each column going across 1, 2, 3, 4, etc.

Then each player can take their own grid and keep it hidden from their opponent as they draw in an agreed selection of battleships. You could each have four battleships that are four squares long, three that are three squares long and two just two squares long.

Each player then takes turns happily yelling out grid references in the hope of hitting some part of their opponent's ships until they have annihilated the entire fleet.

If, however, you choose to have an enormous grid of hundreds of squares and each choose to have just one single battleship two squares long, your game may take quite a long time!

## Letters

Time to draw yet more grids – draw one for each person playing. This time your grids should have boxes large enough for the players to legibly write words inside. You might want to do a grid of perhaps five or more columns going along the top of the page and as many rows as you like below.

Now fill in the top or 'header' row of your grid. Head the first column 'letter' while the others should be given a selection of headings of your choosing such as 'boy's name', 'girl's name', 'colour', 'type of food', 'animal', 'country', etc.

Then choose a random letter from the alphabet and get the players to write it in the 'letter' column of the first row. The game is then for each player to fill in a boy's name, a girl's name, a colour, etc. across the row all starting with this same letter.

## Drawing Without Taking Your Pen Off the Paper

Draw a grid of nine dots in the form of a square (with three dots along each side). Ask your grandchildren to see who can join all nine dots using no more than four straight lines all drawn without lifting their pen from the paper and without going over the same line more than once. Don't give away the secret straight away, but the four straight lines have to be drawn extending beyond the square of dots. Yes, this puzzle quite literally requires you to think outside the box, as shown here:

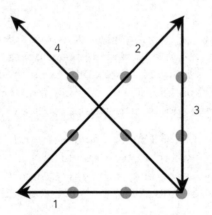

## Squiggles

Quickly draw a squiggly line on your paper. The game is then to use the squiggle and incorporate it into a drawing of something. Alternatively, you can draw someone's initials and turn them into part of a drawing.

# Simple Origami – the Flapping Bird

You may have thought that playing games with bits of paper couldn't get much more exciting – but then along came origami! Kids today may mock the idea of folding pieces of paper into myriad shapes, but try doing it with a mobile phone or tablet and see how far you get! A nice square piece of paper, however, can be transformed into untold treasures. Well, maybe one or two. So here is a reminder of how to make a bird with flapping wings out of a square of paper.

1.  Fold your paper in half diagonally. Unfold it and fold it in half again across the other diagonal. Unfold it once again.

2.  Now fold it in half lengthways. Unfold it and (you've guessed it) fold it in half lengthways across the other length. Unfold it once more! You should now have a square piece of paper which has been folded in half in every possible direction!

3. Fold the paper back into quarters so it forms a small triangle. Open the top flap and fold the top corner to meet the bottom corner; then flip over and do the same on the other side. You should now have all corners of your original piece of paper meeting at the same point.

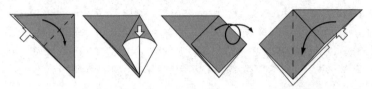

4. Hold this small square you have made in a diamond shape with the four corners of your original piece of paper at the bottom. Fold the edges of your square in to the centre line to form a kite shape and then unfold them back out again. Do this on both sides of your square.

5. Open up the top layer and, using the creases you have just as guidelines, fold the left and right sides into the centre. This will form one of the bird's flapping wings. Do the same on the other side to create the other wing.

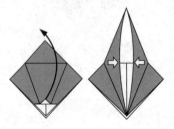

6. Take the top layer from the right side and fold it in to the middle. Do the same for the left-hand side. Then turn the paper over and repeat.

7. The lower flaps of the diamond will form the bird's head and neck and tail. Take one of the flaps and fold it upwards first on one side of the diamond and then the other. Do the same for the other flap. Then open the diamond and pull each flap up between the wings. Finally fold down the end of one of the outer tips to form the head.

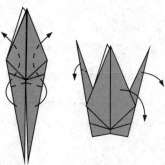

8. Fold up your wings, pull the poor creature's head and tail and watch it flap!

# MAKING UP GAMES IN THE LIVING ROOM

All living rooms contain two types of object: things that can be played with and things that definitely should not be played with. In the latter category, we would include Granny's bone china ornaments, the contents of Granddad's drinks cabinet, the cat or dog's tail, the fire and a few other no-nos.

Otherwise, the living room can be instantly transformed into an adventure playground, an art gallery, a pirate ship, a stage and probably an unholy mess if you're not careful. Still, you're the boss and the possibilities are endless.

The sofa of course can be a boat, surrounded by a carpet of sea, or a sea of carpet if you prefer. The cushions are rowing boats in which people can go ashore to get fresh supplies of food (all the best games involve a snack).

Armchairs, obviously, are racing cars. Brrrm, brrrm!

Tables are places to hide, secret dens, dungeons or simply somewhere more exciting to eat lunch (*underneath* the table, naturally).

Any or all of the above can be commandeered for constructing an obstacle course.

The curtains are of course stage curtains and the fabulous show that the children will put on for you will be performed here. The planning and preparation will hopefully keep them busy while you have forty winks.

Extra supplies can be brought from other rooms, so sheets can be used to build tents or 'camps' and large cardboard boxes can be houses, rooms, prisons, lifts, spaceships and a hundred and one other things. The beauty of it is that you won't need to organise any of this. Provide the raw materials and their imaginations will do the rest.

If the kids want to get creative you probably have an old magazine or two they can cut up to make collages; newspapers are perfect for a bit of origami or for making pirate hats.

The thing is, you see, you've got completely the wrong idea about most of the contents of your living room. Everything is really something else, but you just didn't realise.

# MAKING UP GAMES IN THE KITCHEN

**The list of things that can't be played with in the kitchen is probably a lot longer than the one for the living room, but with a responsible adult in charge – or failing that, a grandparent – everything should be hunky-dory.**

## The Longest Peeling

Even when they're on their own, few adults can resist the temptation to see if they can peel an apple or a potato in one go, thereby producing a length of peel as long as a large intestine. Making this into a competitive sport will keep the kids in quiet, tongue-between-the-teeth concentration for a few precious moments.

## Guess How Much It Weighs

Amazing how a simple set of kitchen scales can provide endless hours of fun with a 'guess the weight' competition. What weighs more – an apple or a banana? How much will a pint of milk weigh? Just try and steer the conversation, though, when the kids want to progress to the bathroom scales to see how much Grandma and Granddad weigh!

## Cake-Making Competitions

If TV can get millions of people to watch other people bake, then surely this will be a fantastic diversion for your little ones. The thing to remember is that when these cakes are cooked you will have to eat them. You have to somehow give the kids the illusion that they have done it all themselves, while you have secretly exercised strict control over the whole process so as not to end up with a cake that contains 14 pounds of sugar and a dollop of curry sauce.

# MAKING UP GAMES ON PUBLIC TRANSPORT

## Spotting Things

It's not just for men in anoraks. Everyone does it all the time, but they just don't know it, and it's easy to turn it into a game. For example, you could see who can spot the most dogs or cats. You could perhaps score extra points for horses. You could look for funny street names, police officers (now there's a challenge!), fire engines – anything you like really. It's amazing how competitive it will get and how much you grandparents will hate losing. First one to 10 or 20, or 50, is the winner.

## Guessing

This is another game with endless variations. You can all make guesses about how long it will take to get to the next stop and the person who is closest is the winner. You can guess how many people will get on or off at the next stop or how many will be men and how many women. The adults can have a little game of their own and guess how many idiotic announcements will be made over the course of the journey and speculate on why you are now called 'customers' instead of 'passengers'.

## Driving

If you are on the top deck of the bus you will of course want to sit at the front and pretend to be the driver, but come on, let the kids have a go too!

## Noughts and Crosses

This can only be played when the bus windows are steamed up and you therefore have a blank canvas for your finger-drawn playing board. And once the game is finished you can wipe the window clean and play some of the other games mentioned above!

## Ticket Origami

Of course, those spoilsports who run public transport these days have virtually done away with proper tickets now. Some of you may even be old enough to remember the bus conductor reeling off a line of tickets a yard long when a family of four was travelling on the bus. Still, if you are lucky enough to get a proper ticket you can see who can make the most impressive bit of origami – and then have to shamefacedly unravel it when the inspector comes to check it!

## Bus Number Bingo

Each person has a piece of paper with the numbers one to nine arranged in three rows: 1, 2, 3; 4, 5, 6; and 7, 8, 9. When you see one of your numbers on a passing bus you circle the appropriate numbers on your piece of paper. So if you see the number 21 bus, you can circle both '1' and '2'. If you eventually circle a whole line you get a small prize and the person who is first to circle all their numbers is the winner. If, however, you live somewhere which only has one bus service a day, it may be some considerable time before anyone wins!

## Train Spotting

Travelling on a train through countryside will increase the opportunities to spot things: horses, sheep, tractors, cows, harvesters, pigs, haystacks, etc. so you can have competitions to see who can spot the most in any category and perhaps even have bonus points for any unusual things like windmills, waterwheels or village pubs that aren't boarded up.

## Tube-Train Sardines

If you ever take the kids into London and go on the tube in the rush hour you will find you are playing an impromptu game of Sardines. The rule are that there are no rules, and there are no winners. Everyone gets squashed! You will also be able to play the game of 'Which station are we at now?' as the train is so packed you can't see out of the window.

## Alphabet Game

Taking it in turns, each person has to spot something out of the window first beginning with A, then B and so on. Special prizes can be given to those spotting things beginning with Q, X and Z!

# GAMES TO PLAY IN THE CAR

There are further opportunities for fun games if you have to drive the grandchildren somewhere. Once again, the grandkids may whip out their tablets and phones to provide their own in-drive entertainment before you turn the ignition. But just in case their batteries are running flat, there are games old and new that can be played while you're all stuck in traffic.

Obviously, some games detailed elsewhere in this book can also be played while trapped inside cars. I Spy and Twenty Questions are perennial favourites for those on the move.

On the other hand, games such as Hide and Seek should probably not be attempted while you are driving – especially if you are stuck in a queue and the children are able to open the doors and leave the vehicle while you're not looking.

Otherwise, you should be reasonably safe with the following!

## Number–Plate Sentences

There are a number of games based around number plates. One of the most popular is to challenge the kids to make up a sentence using the letters on a passing car's number plate as the initial letters of the words in the sentence. Don't bother trying to use the numbers as well because that would probably make it a bit too tricky. But if, for example, you saw a number plate that reads KP65 UXL, a possible sentence might be 'Kevin plays unusual xylophone lullabies' or 'Katie Price uses x-ray lanterns'. A competitive element can be added by challenging players to see who can come up with a sentence based on the letters on a chosen number plate in the fastest time.

## Number–Plate Mathematics

If anyone feels the numbers on the passing number plates are being overlooked in the Number-Plate Sentences game, you can play Number-Plate Maths. Who will be first to add up or multiply together all the numbers on a passing number plate?

## Number–Plate Bingo

This game requires a little bit more setting up. Give each child in the car a piece of paper with a word or series of words written on it. Each child gets a different word or set of words. Short words such as 'boat' or 'cat' might be appropriate for small children. Longer words such as 'counter-revolutionary' or 'electroencephalogram' may be suitable for older children or adults or if you are on a particularly agonisingly long journey. The game is then for the child to cross off letters in their word(s) every time they see them on a passing number plate. The first to cross off all their letters is the winner.

This game probably kept kids happy for hours in the good old days when there wasn't much traffic around. Today you could probably go out in the rush hour and they'll have got through 'antidisestablishmentarianism' before you've pulled out of the top of your road!

## Car Colours

Incredibly simple! Just get each kid to choose a different colour. The game is then for each child to spot and count up vehicles of that colour. Whoever spots the most cars in their chosen colour during the course of your excursion is the winner. The colours chosen should preferably be ones conceivably used for a car's bodywork. If anyone chooses ultraviolet or luminous pink they are unlikely to win the game. On the other hand, if they choose white or black they may tot up hundreds within a few minutes of leaving home. Maybe stick to likely but slightly less common colours such as red or blue. If you want to make it a bit more challenging you could tell one child to look for orange cars and another for green cars.

## Who Can Spot...?

Another variation of the car-spotting game is to give each child their own type of object to look out for during the journey. One child perhaps has to look out for nodding model animals on the back shelf of passing cars, another has to look out for drivers wearing caps and so on.

## Foreign Cars

If you are doing a longer journey you could play a game of spotting cars from overseas. The challenge is for the grandkids to identify any vehicles that have signs on their number plates or elsewhere denoting that they are from foreign countries. They may need some help to identify where the car is from by means of the abbreviations used for each country – so you may have to do a bit of preparatory homework learning all of those! The game could then be who can spot the car or lorry that has come from furthest away. Your journey will thus provide an exciting lesson in world geography and the joys of car registration!

# MAKING THINGS OUT OF PAPER, STUFF AND GENERAL RUBBISH

The refuse collectors will wonder why your recycling bin is virtually empty these days and suspect you of naughtily putting your recyclables in with the general rubbish. But no, you are doing the ultimate in recycling – you are turning your rubbish into heavenly gifts for your grandchildren. Well, a bit of fun anyway... Suddenly, you will realise that everything you previously thought of as rubbish is now something to keep the kids amused for hours. Old newspapers, magazines, cereal boxes, tin cans, toilet roll tubes, milk bottles, cardboard boxes – it's all grandchild gold dust!

## Milk–Bottle Xylophones

Get half a dozen or so glass bottles or jars, fill them with varying amounts of water and arrange them in a line from least full to most full. Then tap them with a wooden spoon to produce musical notes – in a scale! Before long you and they will be knocking out tunes like Billy-o, or possibly even Billy Joel. Warning – do not use this game as an excuse to try and get through multiple bottles of vino the night before the grandkids arrive!

## Tin–Can Telephones

Do we need to tell you that this is two empty tin cans connected with thread? Of course, many children today have mobile phones and you might think that the delights of a tin can telephone would be lost on them, but you would be wrong. The magical transformation of a couple of old baked bean containers into a communications device will amaze them. It will also confuse them when they realise you don't have to charge it before use or take out a contract.

## A Home of Their Own!

Next time you have a large item delivered, such as a fridge, keep the massive box because this will be a fabulous investment in childhood happiness. It can be an impromptu Wendy house, spaceship, log cabin, pirate ship, dungeon, castle, penthouse flat or a hundred and one other pieces of real estate. They will probably even want to eat their lunch in there so all the mess will be nicely contained!

## Toilet-Roll Tubes

These are to children's entertainment what the humble house brick is to the construction industry – a basic but vital component. They can be the bodies of dolls or robots, pipelines, components of marble mazes, Doric columns for posh doll's houses, ear trumpets, binoculars, skittles, field dressings for fingers 'wounded' in battle, rolling pins, limbs for puppets, anything you like really. How on earth did children play before the toilet roll was invented?

## Treasure Boxes

One man's rubbish is another kid's treasure, right? And what could be better than for each child to make their own treasure box? Simply get a cardboard box – maybe an old cereal packet – and cut a hole in it so it looks a bit like a TV (if desired, you could cut it so there is an opening 'lid' to the box). It can then be painted inside and filled with bits of 'treasure'. This could be bits of old jewellery, coins, photographs of family members or pets, pictures from magazines, etc. These can then be stuck into the box so the child has their own personalised treasure box.

## Collages

When all else fails, this is the humdinger of rubbish recycling. Old magazines, newspapers, cereal boxes, bits of material, buttons, junk mail (at last, there's a use for it!), milk bottle lids – it is all grist to the collage mill. The kids, and you, will have hours of fun gluing all this stuff onto a big sheet of paper or card and then showing the results to the proud parents. Who knows, you might even win the Turner Prize.

## Pirate Hats

Take a piece of newspaper and fold it in half. Then, fold down the two top corners to meet in the middle. The top of the paper should now be pyramid-shaped, and there should be a section of unfolded paper sticking out at the bottom on each side. Take one of the bottom sections of paper and fold it up over the pyramid-shape. Repeat on the other side and – shiver me timbers! – you have a pirate hat! Draw on a skull and crossbones or paint according to taste.

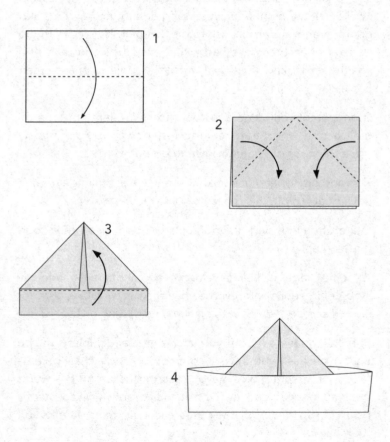

# THINGS THAT KIDS AND GRANDPARENTS HAVE IN COMMON

Despite the age difference, kids and grandparents have more in common than you think. They are both quite often up to something the parents don't approve of, whether it's eating and drinking things that aren't good for them or staying awake half the night and catnapping during the day. Kids and grandparents are also conspirators, keeping it quiet from the parents when they have had a burger and fries instead of a healthy meal, and they think a toffee apple is one of their five-a-day.

Grandparents and kids also seem to have plenty of time on their hands, which they seem to fritter away quite carelessly while the poor old parents have to go out to work.

Kids and grandparents also know how to use their age to their advantage. 'Ooh, this is heavy – can you lift it for me?'

Quite often kids and grandparents will both need their food mashing up.

At some stage in their development, grandparents suddenly stop being adults and revert to being children with a taste for sweets and ice creams, cartoon films and playing on the swings.

Perhaps, above all, both you and your grandchildren will be united because you have a common enemy – their parents (aka your offspring plus maybe their partner). And this works out well for everyone involved as the parent(s) will constantly be trying to get both their kids and you, their parents, off their hands.

And that's not all that grandparents and grandchildren have in common. You're both probably short of money while feeling as though you're powerless and ignored by patronising individuals who want to make all your decisions for you.

The world is full of new and exciting things for children because they're young and haven't experienced everything yet. And the same is true for grandparents because everything in the world that you knew from your younger days has now been improved and/or computerised and/or replaced by something less good and specifically designed to drive you crazy.

# JOKES AND RIDDLES FOR KIDS

Have you noticed that everyone groans at Christmas cracker jokes – apart from kids? Christmas cracker jokes are perfect for kids – simple, daft, corny; in fact, all the things that adults think they have grown out of but haven't really. This is why adults groan at them, because they're telling the world they are far too sophisticated to go for such stuff. They also pretend not to like kids' TV programmes, cartoons, beans on toast and sticky sweets. They're lying.

The sort of jokes that kids like fall into the following categories:

## Nonsensical Jokes

Young kids especially will sometimes invent their own jokes which seem to make no sense at all. For example:

Q. Why did the chicken cross the road?

A. Because it's a saucepan.

Whether they will accept this kind of joke from an adult, though, is another matter entirely.

## Knock–Knock Jokes

Kids love formats and repetition, so once they understand the format of the knock-knock joke, they won't be able to get enough of them.

## Animal Jokes

All kids love animals, partly because their pet cat never tells them to tidy their room, and their pet hamster never makes them eat broccoli. So any joke involving animals is going to go down well. Some grandparents might remember the craze for elephant jokes in their youth, so maybe they could dredge up a few of those from their memories.

## Jokes That Won't Work

It's no good telling them the one about the Englishman, the Irishman and the Scotsman, because as far as kids are concerned they're all adults and therefore completely beyond their understanding.

## Awful Puns

Young kids are still getting to grips with the language and so for them it's a first-time delight to realise that 'I saw my granddad' might bring to mind poor old Granddad lying on a workbench with someone brandishing a hacksaw above his tummy. Similarly, when someone says 'the dog pants' it might conjure up hilarious images of a pet Chihuahua in Y-fronts.

# QUESTION–AND–ANSWER JOKES

Kids love jokes. They even love jokes that don't make them laugh very much. They will nevertheless commit these to memory as though they were holy writ, with a view to using them to impress their friends at school or elsewhere.

Question-and-answer-style jokes are particularly popular as posing the question provides small kids with a delicious moment of supremacy over their fellows. Unfortunately, even the smallest children will be aware from birth of why chickens cross roads or how your dog smells despite having no nasal orifice.

Here, though, are some reminders of a few other old chestnuts you could share with the grandkids:

### What did the hat say to the scarf?

'You hang around while I go on ahead.'

### What happens when a clock is hungry?

It goes back four seconds.

### Why do bees hum?

They don't know the words.

**What happened when the dog
went to the flea circus?**

He stole the show!

••••••••••••••••••

**What has four legs and a trunk?**

A mouse going off on his holidays.

••••••••••••••••••

**What does a horse say when it
steps out of the fridge?**

'Brrrrrrrrrrrrrrrr.'

••••••••••••••••••

**What does a dog become after
it is six years old?**

Seven years old.

••••••••••••••••••

**What gets smaller the more
you put in it?**

A hole in the ground!

**Why do birds fly south in the winter?**

Because it's too far to walk.

•••••••••••••••••

**What has two tails, two trunks
and five feet?**

An elephant with spare parts.

•••••••••••••••••

**What has four legs and flies?**

A dead horse. (Or two pairs of trousers!)

•••••••••••••••••

**What do you get when you drop a
piano on an army headquarters?**

A flat major.

•••••••••••••••••

**What do you get when you throw a
piano down a mineshaft?**

A flat miner.

There are of course lots of variations available on the old 'crossing the road' joke, such as:

### Why did the one-handed man cross the road?

To get to the second-hand shop.

••••••••••••••••

### Why did the dinosaur cross the road?

Because chickens hadn't been invented yet.

••••••••••••••••

### Why did the chicken cross the road?

Don't ask me – ask the chicken.

Another irresistible form of the question-and-answer joke is 'What do you get if you cross...' in which we can explore a series of terrible genetic experiments on different creatures. For example:

**What do you get if you cross
a kangaroo and a sheep?**

A woolly jumper!

**What do you get when you cross
a strawberry with a road?**

A traffic jam!

**What do you get when you cross
a kangaroo with an elephant?**

Great big holes all over Australia!

**What do you get if you cross
a chicken with a cement mixer?**

A brick layer!

•••••••••••••••••

**What do you get if you cross
a dog and a sheep?**

A sheep that can round itself up!

•••••••••••••••••

**What do you get when you cross
an octopus with a cow?**

An animal that can milk itself!

•••••••••••••••••

**What do you get if you cross a cocker
spaniel with a poodle and a rooster?**

A cockapoodledoo!

•••••••••••••••••

**What do you get if you cross
a cat with a canary?**

Shredded tweet!

**What do you get if you cross an artist with a policeman?**

A brush with the law!

•••••••••••••••••

**What do you get if you cross an overweight golfer and a pair of very tight trousers?**

A hole in one!

•••••••••••••••••

**What do you get if you cross the Atlantic Ocean with the Titanic?**

About halfway across!

•••••••••••••••••

**What do you get when you cross a wolf and an egg?**

A very hairy omelette!

**What do you get if you cross
a cow with a trampoline?**

A milkshake!

●●●●●●●●●●●●●●●●●

**What do you get if you cross
a parrot with a shark?**

A bird that will talk your ear off!

●●●●●●●●●●●●●●●●●

**What do you get when you cross
a ghost and a cat?**

A scaredy cat!

●●●●●●●●●●●●●●●●●

**What do you get when you cross
a potato with an elephant?**

Mashed potatoes!

●●●●●●●●●●●●●●●●●

**What do you get when you cross
a karate expert with a pig?**

A pork chop!

**What do you get when you cross
a cow and a lawnmower?**

A lawnmooer!

•••••••••••••••••

**What do you get when you cross
a snake and a pie?**

A pie-thon!

•••••••••••••••••

**What do you get if you cross
a centipede and a parrot?**

A walkie-talkie!

•••••••••••••••••

**What do you get when you cross
a dinosaur with a pig?**

Jurassic Pork!

And let's not forget the 'What do you call a person…' jokes. Why not get the grandchildren to try making some more jokes along the same lines using the names of people they know?!

### What do you call a man in a brown paper suit?

Russell.

•••••••••••••••

### What do you call a woman who stands next to walls?

Eileen.

•••••••••••••••

### What do you call a man in a cooking pot?

Stu.

•••••••••••••••

### What do you call a woman who stands between two goal posts?

Annette.

**What do you call a man
with three eyes?**

Seymour.

•••••••••••••••

**What do you call a man who
wears two coats?**

Max.

•••••••••••••••

**What do you call a man with no legs?**

Neil.

•••••••••••••••

**What do you call a man with no shins?**

Tony.

•••••••••••••••

**What do you call a French
man in sandals?**

Philippe Philoppe.

**What do you call a man with a
tree growing out of his head?**

Edward.

•••••••••••••••••

**What do you call a man lying
by a front door?**

Matt.

•••••••••••••••••

**What do you call a man
sitting in a hole?**

Phil.

•••••••••••••••••

**What do you call a woman with
a sheep on her head?**

Baa-Baa-Ra.

# KNOCK, KNOCK

More plays on various people's names can be found in another staple format – the knock-knock joke! Again, it's great for kids because of the strict wording of the format, the fact that you have no choice but to fall in and say your bit of the joke and of course the utterly stupid twist that follows. It's like early training for kids on how to perform scripted dialogue! Here are some famous examples:

**Knock, knock.**

Who's there?

**Abby.**

Abby who?

**Abby birthday to you!**

•••••••••••••••••

**Knock, knock.**

Who's there?

**Justin.**

Justin who?

**Just in time for dinner.**

**Knock, knock.**

Who's there?

**Arthur.**

Arthur who?

**Arthur any biscuits left
in the cupboard?**

•••••••••••••••••

**Knock, knock.**

Who's there?

**Isabel.**

Isabel who?

**Isabel necessary on a bicycle?**

•••••••••••••••••

**Knock, knock.**

Who's there?

**Amos.**

Amos who?

**A mosquito.**

**Knock, knock.**

Who's there?

**Nanna.**

Nanna who?

**Nanna your business.**

•••••••••••••••••

**Knock, knock.**

Who's there?

**Anita.**

Anita who?

**Anita tissue... Ah-choo! Too late!**

•••••••••••••••••

**Knock, knock.**

Who's there?

**Howard.**

Howard who?

**Howard I know?**

There are even whole swathes of knock-knock jokes that get a lot of silly fun out of the idea of answering the door:

**Knock, knock.**

Who's there?

**Honey bee.**

Honey bee who?

**Honey bee a dear and open this door!**

•••••••••••••••

**Knock, knock.**

Who's there?

**A herd.**

A herd who?

**A herd you were home,
so I came to see you!**

•••••••••••••••

**Knock, knock.**

Who's there?

**Adore.**

Adore who?

**Adore is between us so
hurry up and open it!**

**Knock, knock.**

Who's there?

**Kanye.**

Kanye who?

**Kanye come out to play!**

•••••••••••••••••

**Knock, knock.**

Who's there?

**Thedora.**

Thedora who?

**Thedora is locked – could you
please come and open it!**

•••••••••••••••••

**Knock, knock.**

Who's there?

**Annie.**

Annie who?

**Annie chance you could let me in?
It's freezing out here!**

The knock-knock format also provides opportunities for that much-loved icing on the joke-telling cake – the funny voice:

**Knock, knock.**

Who's there?

**Matthew.**

Matthew who?

**Matthew lathe hath come undone.**

•••••••••••••••••

**Knock, knock.**

Who's there?

**Dwayne.**

Dwayne who?

**Dwayne the bathtub, it's overflowing!**

•••••••••••••••••

**Knock, knock.**

Who's there?

**Euripides.**

Euripides who?

**Euripides jeans, you pay for 'em, OK?**

And if that's not silly enough, knock-knock jokes sometimes reach positively postmodern levels!

**Knock, knock.**

Who's there?

**A little man who can't
reach the doorbell!**

●●●●●●●●●●●●●●●●●

**Knock, knock.**

Who's there?

**Tank.**

Tank who?

**Don't mention it! You're welcome!**

●●●●●●●●●●●●●●●●●

**Knock, knock.**

Who's there?

**Doorbell.**

Doorbell who?

**Doorbell repair man!**

**Knock, knock.**

Who's there?

**Repeat.**

Repeat who?

**Who who who who.**

●●●●●●●●●●●●●●●

**Knock, knock.**

Who's there?

**The interrupting cow.**

The interrupting cow wh…

**Moooooo!**

●●●●●●●●●●●●●●●

**Knock, knock.**

Who's there?

**Little old lady.**

Little old lady who?

**I didn't know you could yodel.**

**Knock, knock.**

Who's there?

**Spell.**

Spell who?

**OK – W. H. O.**

•••••••••••••••••••

**Knock, knock.**

Who's there?

**Boo.**

Boo who?

**OK, no need to cry – it's only a joke.**

There's even a knock-knock joke to try and shut the little darlings up when you're feeling absolutely sick of knock-knock jokes!

**Knock, knock.**

Who's there?

**Evan.**

Evan who?

**Evan you heard enough of all these silly knock-knock jokes?**

Unfortunately, the answer may possibly be 'No'!

# RIDDLES

Riddles are jokes that seem to make no effort whatsoever to be funny. They still manage to get away with it, however, because they are very ancient and involve homely old objects and concepts that your grandkids may not normally deal with on a regular basis – such as candles, needles, rivers, mountains and the outdoors generally. Most importantly, riddles provide great fun to puzzle over, and what's more you can set the grandchildren the task of coming up with some new modern ones to try and trick you back. The answers to the following riddles are given at the end of this section in case you'd like to solve them yourselves:

1.  A box without hinges, key or lid, yet golden treasure inside is hid. What am I?

2.  Give me food, and I will live; give me water, and I will die. What am I?

3.  I'm tall when I'm young and I'm short when I'm old. What am I?

4.  What has one eye but cannot see?

5.  Thirty white horses on a red hill: first they champ, then they stamp, then they stand still. What are they?

6.  What can you hold without using your hands or arms?

7.  What is so fragile that even saying its name will break it?

8.  I'm as flat as a leaf, round as a ring; I have two eyes, but can't see a thing. What am I?

9.  I can run but not walk. Wherever I go, thought follows me close behind. What am I?

10. It goes through the door without pinching. It sits on the stove without burning. It sits on the table not ashamed. What is it?

11. I build up castles. I tear down mountains. I make some blind and I help others see. What am I?

12. Whoever makes it, tells it not. Whoever accepts it, knows it not. And whoever knows it, wants it not. What is it?

13. What has to be broken before it can be used?

14. I am a box that holds keys without locks and yet my keys will unlock your deepest senses. What am I?

15. It walks on four legs in the morning, two legs at noon and three legs in the evening. What is it?

16. What always runs but never walks, often murmurs, never talks, has a bed but never sleeps, has a mouth but never eats?

17. At night they come without being fetched. By day they are lost without being stolen. What are they?

18. The one who makes it, sells it. The one who buys it, never uses it. The one that uses it never knows that they are using it. What is it?

19. The more you have of it, the less you see. What is it?

20. It cannot be seen, it weighs nothing, but when put into a barrel, it makes it lighter. What is it?

21. I'm full of holes, yet I'm full of water. What am I?

22. What has hands but cannot clap?

23. Take off my skin – I won't cry, but you will! What am I?

24. What has a neck and no head, two arms but no hands?

25. Pronounced as one letter, but written with three, two letters there are, only two in me. I'm double, I'm single, I'm black, blue and grey, I'm read from both ends and the same either way. What am I?

26. It is greater than God, more evil than the devil, the poor have it, the rich need it, and if you eat it you'll die. What is it?

27. **What can travel around the world while staying in a corner?**

28. You can drop me from the tallest building and I'll be fine, but if you drop me in water I die. What am I?

29. **It is as light as a feather, but even the world's strongest man cannot hold it for more than a couple of minutes. What is it?**

## Answers to the Riddles

1. An egg.

2. A fire.

3. A candle (or maybe it's Granddad or Grandma!).

4. A needle.

5. Teeth.

6. Your breath.

7. Silence.

8. A button.

9. A nose.

10. The sun.

11. Sand.

12. Fake money.

13. An egg.

14. A piano.

15. Man.

16. A river.

17. The stars.

18. A coffin.

19. Darkness.

20. A hole.

21. A sponge.

22. A clock.

23. An onion.

24. A shirt.

25. An eye.

26. Nothing.

27. A stamp.

28. Paper.

29. Breath.

## REALLY SILLY JOKES

When it comes to jokes that will appeal to kids, the sillier the better. Not only will the grandkids take delight in mystifying anyone they tell these jokes to, but they can go on to reveal a punchline that is extraordinarily stupid, leaving the bamboozled parent, friend, teacher (or other poor unfortunate who has been subjected to the joke) feeling utterly foolish they didn't guess it. What could be more perfect?!

**What do you call a fish with no eyes?**

A fsh.

•••••••••••••••••

**What do you call a pig with three eyes?**

A piiig.

•••••••••••••••••

**What do you call a fly with no wings?**

A walk.

•••••••••••••••••

**What do you find in the middle of a jellyfish?**

A jellybutton.

**What's white and fluffy
and beats its chest?**

A meringue-utan.

●●●●●●●●●●●●●●●●

**What do you call a deer with no eyes?**

No idea.

●●●●●●●●●●●●●●●●

**What do you call a sleeping
deer with no eyes?**

Still no idea.

●●●●●●●●●●●●●●●●

**What do you call a chicken
at the North Pole?**

Lost.

●●●●●●●●●●●●●●●●

**Why are pirates called pirates?**

They just arrrrrrrrrrrrrrrrrrrrr!

**Why are bears large, brown and hairy?**

Because if they were small, white and
smooth they'd be eggs.

•••••••••••••••••

**What's brown and sticky?**

A stick.

•••••••••••••••••

**What do you call a boomerang
that doesn't come back?**

A stick.

•••••••••••••••••

**What do you call a donkey
with three legs?**

A wonkey.

•••••••••••••••••

**What do you get if you cross
a dog with a frog?**

A dog that can lick you from
the other side of the road!

**What has two humps and is
found at the North Pole?**

A camel that's lost.

●●●●●●●●●●●●●●●

**What's the best way to catch a gorilla?**

Hide in a tree and make
a noise like a banana.

●●●●●●●●●●●●●●●

**What's the difference between
an elephant and a flea?**

An elephant can have fleas but
a flea can't have elephants.

●●●●●●●●●●●●●●●

**What's smelly, round and laughs?**

A tickled onion.

●●●●●●●●●●●●●●●

**Where do you go to weigh a pie?**

Somewhere over the rainbow.

**What's a myth?**

A female moth!

••••••••••••••••••

**What's big, green and can't fly?**

A field.

••••••••••••••••••

**Why did the parrot wear a raincoat?**

So he would be polyunsaturated.

And if you want to make your jokes even sillier and even more annoying, the relentless repetition of certain themes can help! Exhibit one – the classic elephant joke:

**How do you know when there is
an elephant in your bed?**

There's an 'E' on the front of its pyjamas.

••••••••••••••••••

**How do you know if there is an
elephant under the bed?**

Your nose is pressed up
against the ceiling.

### How do you get four elephants in a Mini?

Two in the front and two in the back.

•••••••••••••••••

### How many giraffes can you fit in a Mini?

You can't – it's full up with elephants.

•••••••••••••••••

### What time is it when an elephant sits on the fence?

Time to get a new fence!

•••••••••••••••••

### What would you call a friend who had an elephant on his head?

A flat mate.

•••••••••••••••••

### Why do elephants paint the soles of their feet yellow?

So that they can hide upside down in bowls of custard.

**How do you get an
elephant out of a tree?**

Get it to stand on a leaf
and wait till autumn.

••••••••••••••••••

**Why couldn't the two elephants
go swimming together?**

They only had one pair
of trunks between them.

••••••••••••••••••

**What should you do if you find an
elephant asleep on your bed?**

Sleep on the sofa.

••••••••••••••••••

**How can you tell if an elephant is
sitting behind you in a bathtub?**

You can smell the peanuts on his breath.

**What do elephants have for lunch?**

Half an hour, just like everybody else.

•••••••••••••••••

**What has two grey legs
and two brown legs?**

An elephant that didn't
get to the toilet in time.

•••••••••••••••••

**What's the difference between an
elephant's backside and a letter box?**

If you don't know, I'm definitely not
giving you my letter to post!

And there are even elephant jokes which don't mention
elephants at all:

**How do you get six donkeys
into a fire engine?**

Two in the front, two in the back and two
on the top going, 'He-haw, he-haw!'

## APPALLING PUNS

In their quest for the arcane knowledge contained in bad old jokes, kids will relish an appalling pun above all else. Warning – your grandchildren will find these jokes increasingly unimpressive the older they get, so don't expect a positive response if you try telling them when they have reached their late teenage years!

**When is a door not a door?**

When it's ajar.

●●●●●●●●●●●●●●●●●●

**What's the quickest way to make anti-freeze?**

Hide her nightie.

●●●●●●●●●●●●●●●●●●

**What did the big bucket say to the little bucket?**

'You look a little pail.'

●●●●●●●●●●●●●●●●●●

**Why was six frightened?**

Because seven eight nine.

**Where do generals keep their armies?**

Up their sleevies.

•••••••••••••••••

**What's a polygon?**

A dead parrot.

•••••••••••••••••

**What do you call the place where parrots make films?**

Pollywood.

•••••••••••••••••

**Which cowboy lives at the bottom of the sea?**

Billy the Squid.

•••••••••••••••••

**Who was the first person to wear a shell suit?**

Humpty Dumpty.

## JOKES THAT TRICK THE PERSON YOU'RE TALKING TO INTO SAYING SOMETHING THAT WILL MAKE THEM LOOK SILLY

As you may have realised by now, the main purpose of jokes for small children is not to amuse anyone but rather to make the person they're telling the joke to look a bit foolish. Indeed, some jokes are specifically designed to accomplish this very purpose. These little routines are crafted to trick the person being spoken to into saying something self-derogatory and/or to generally make a complete fool of themselves. This of course is absolutely hilarious for children – although possibly less hilarious for the person who is being told the joke. They stand there expecting to be told some entertaining and chucklesome witticism but instead find the joke is in fact themselves! The following may all therefore seem a bit cruel. But don't worry. Look on them as a series of early lessons in human psychology for your grandkids!

**Spell the word 'pots'.**

P-O-T-S.

**Spell it again!**

P-O-T-S.

**What do you do when you get to a green traffic light?**

Stop.

**No! Green means 'go'! I'm not going in the car if you're driving!**

**Spell the word 'ghost'.**

G-H-O-S-T.

**Now spell the word 'most'.**

M-O-S-T.

**Now spell the word 'roast'.**

R-O-A-S-T.

**What's the thing you put in a toaster?**

Toast!

**No! It's bread! No one puts
toast in a toaster!**

●●●●●●●●●●●●●●●●

**What does M-A-C-D-O-N-A-L-D spell?**

MacDonald.

**What does M-A-C-G-R-E-G-O-R spell?**

MacGregor.

**What does M-A-C-H-I-N-E-R-Y spell?**

Mac-Hinery.

**No! It spells machinery! Who's ever
heard of anyone called Mac-Hinery?!**

**Spell the word 'folk'.**

F-O-L-K.

**Spell the word 'joke'.**

J-O-K-E.

**Spell the word 'poke'.**

P-O-K-E.

**What's the white of an egg called?**

Yolk.

**No! The yolk is the yellowy bit!**

•••••••••••••••

**What does R-O-U-G-H spell?**

Rough.

**What does T-O-U-G-H spell?**

Tough.

**What does D-O-U-G-H spell?**

Duff.

**No! It's pronounced 'dough'!**

Of course, only the very gullible will fall for many of these tricks if you try to play them one after another. It may therefore be necessary to try some other methods to make them look silly!

**What's the difference between an elephant and a matterbaby?**

What's a matterbaby?

**Nothing, honey. What's-a-matter with you?**

●●●●●●●●●●●●●●●●●

**If a red house is made with red bricks, a blue house is made with blue bricks, a pink house is made with pink bricks, a black house is made with black bricks, what is a green house made with?**

Green bricks.

**No! It's made of glass!**

**Want to hear an alternative
'knock-knock' joke?**

OK.

**OK. You start…**

Knock, knock.

**Who's there?**

Er…

•••••••••••••••••

**What do you think T-W-A spells?**

Twaa!

**What does T-W-E spell?**

Twee!

**What does T-W-I spell?**

Twy!

**So what does T-W-O spell?**

Twoah!

**No! It spells 'two'!**

And let's not forget the absolute gold dust of kids' jokes – the opportunity to mention going to the toilet! Or even better, to get someone else to unwittingly announce their toilet-going habits to the world!

**Knock, knock.**

Who's there?

**Ivedonnap.**

Ivedonnap who?

**Well flush the toilet and let me in then!
And don't forget to wash
your hands first!**

*Or if a particularly small child is telling the joke, the final line is more likely to be:*

**Poo! You've done a poo!
You just said you did a poo!**

••••••••••••••••••

**Knock, knock.**

Who's there?

**Europe.**

Europe who?

**I'm not a poo. You are.**

*Less punningly, but more directly and hilariously, the person knocking may of course be called 'I-map' or even 'I-smellop'!*

# JOKES YOU THINK YOU SHOULD KNOW THE ANSWER TO BUT DON'T

Another way to make the person you're talking to look a bit stupid is to ask them a question they think they have a good chance of getting the answer to. Maybe it's a very simple question. Or a joke they think they have heard before. And then you can once again pull the rug from under their feet by giving them the correct answer!

**What do you get hanging from cherry trees?**

Sore arms.

●●●●●●●●●●●●●●●●

**Why are there so many people called Smith in the phone book?**

They all have phones.

●●●●●●●●●●●●●●●●

**Where do you find the most fish?**

Between the head and tail.

**What's black and white and read all over?**

A newspaper.

●●●●●●●●●●●●●●●●

**What's black and white and red all over?**

A Dalmatian with sunburn.

●●●●●●●●●●●●●●●●

**What is half of infinity?**

Nity.

●●●●●●●●●●●●●●●●

**Why did Robin Hood rob from the rich?**

Because the poor didn't have anything worth stealing!

●●●●●●●●●●●●●●●●

**Where was the Magna Carta signed?**

At the bottom!

**What has 50 legs but can't walk?**

Half a centipede!

● ● ● ● ● ● ● ● ● ● ● ● ● ● ● ●

**What is the only true cure for dandruff?**

Baldness.

● ● ● ● ● ● ● ● ● ● ● ● ● ● ● ●

**What lies on its back
100 feet in the air?**

A centipede.

● ● ● ● ● ● ● ● ● ● ● ● ● ● ● ●

**What looks like half a cat?**

The other half.

● ● ● ● ● ● ● ● ● ● ● ● ● ● ● ●

**What's orange and sounds
like a parrot?**

A carrot.

**What sort of animal is a slug?**

A snail with a housing problem.

••••••••••••••••••

**What should you buy if
your hair falls out?**

A good vacuum cleaner.

••••••••••••••••••

**What's a quark?**

The noise made by a very posh duck.

••••••••••••••••••

**What's green and looks like a bucket?**

A green bucket.

••••••••••••••••••

**What's blue and smells of red paint?**

Blue paint.

**What's pink and fluffy?**

Pink fluff.

••••••••••••••••

**What's red and white?**

Pink!

••••••••••••••••

**What's the best way to stop water
coming into your house?**

Don't pay the water bill.

••••••••••••••••

**What's the quickest way to
double your money?**

Fold it in half!

••••••••••••••••

**When did Julius Caesar die?**

A few days before his funeral!

**When does a dog go 'Moo'?**

When it's learning a second language!

• • • • • • • • • • • • • • •

**Where are the Seychelles?**

On the sey shore.

• • • • • • • • • • • • • • •

**Where do you find a
tortoise with no legs?**

Exactly where you left it.

• • • • • • • • • • • • • • •

**Where do you find giant snails?**

On the ends of their fingers.

• • • • • • • • • • • • • • •

**Which two words in the English
language have the most letters?**

Post office!

**Why do dogs wag their tails?**

No one else will do it for them!

•••••••••••••••••

**Why do giraffes have such long necks?**

Because their feet smell.

•••••••••••••••••

**Why do polar bears have fur coats?**

Because they would look silly in anoraks.

•••••••••••••••••

**Why does a flamingo lift up one leg?**

Because if it lifted up both
it would fall over.

•••••••••••••••••

**Why hasn't anyone ever stolen a canal?**

They have too many locks.

# JOKES TO MAKE CHILDREN SCREAM

Another popular category for the little ones will be what they regard as jokes about the most horrific things in the world. These could involve monsters, vampires or ghosts. Alternatively, it could be creepy-crawlies, animals likely to eat you or, even better, bogies and unfortunate bodily functions! For added hilarity, try saying the punchlines in an appropriately scary manner!

**What did the mummy ghost
say to the baby ghost?**

Don't spook until you're spoken to.

•••••••••••••••

**Why did the ghost go to the doctor?**

To get his boo-ster shot.

•••••••••••••••

**Who did the ghost take to the dance?**

His ghoul friend.

•••••••••••••••

**What do you get if you cross
a dog and a lion?**

A terrified postman!

**What do you call a haunted chicken?**

A poultry geist.

•••••••••••••••••

**What kind of mistakes
do spooks make?**

Boo boos.

•••••••••••••••••

**What did the monster eat after having
his teeth fixed by his dentist?**

His dentist.

•••••••••••••••••

**What does the ghost of a parrot say?**

Oooooooooooo's a pretty boy then?!

•••••••••••••••••

**Why are there fences
around cemeteries?**

Because people are dying to get in.

**Why don't skeletons like parties?**

They have no body to dance with.

••••••••••••••••••

**Why don't skeletons like
to eat spicy food?**

They can't stomach it!

••••••••••••••••••

**Why was the student vampire
tired in the morning?**

Because he was up all night studying
for his blood test!

••••••••••••••••••

**Why doesn't Dracula have any friends?**

Because he's a pain in the neck!

**What type of coffee
do vampires prefer?**

Decoffinated.

●●●●●●●●●●●●●●●●

**Where does Count Dracula
make his withdrawals?**

At the blood bank.

●●●●●●●●●●●●●●●●

**What do you call a deaf monster?**

Whatever you like – he can't hear you!

●●●●●●●●●●●●●●●●

**What do you get if you cross
a cat with a monster?**

A town remarkably free of dogs.

●●●●●●●●●●●●●●●●

**What's 12 feet long, has big teeth and
eats people while going up and down?**

A shark in a lift.

**What kind of monster sticks
to the end of your finger?**

The bogey man.

•••••••••••••••••

**What do you get if you cross an
anthill with a packet of seeds?**

Ants in your plants.

•••••••••••••••••

**What's got 1,000 legs and 1,000 teeth
and a great big scary face?**

I don't know but one just crawled down
your neck and went inside your collar.

•••••••••••••••••

**What has four legs and says 'Boo'?**

A cow with a cold.

**What did the man say when he saw a dinosaur coming down the path wearing sunglasses?**

Nothing! He didn't recognise him.

•••••••••••••••••

**Why shouldn't you do your sums in the jungle?**

Because if you add four to four you get ate!

•••••••••••••••••

**What do you get if you cross a spider and an elephant?**

I'm not sure, but if you see one walking across the ceiling, run before it falls on you.

•••••••••••••••••

**What would happen if tarantulas were as big as horses?**

If one bit you, you could ride it to hospital!

**What do you get if you
cross a cat and a gorilla?**

An animal that puts you out at night!

••••••••••••••••••

**What do you get if you cross a
daffodil with a crocodile?**

I don't know but I wouldn't try sniffing it!

••••••••••••••••••

**Why do gorillas have big nostrils?**

Because they have big fingers.

••••••••••••••••••

**What's worse than finding a
maggot in your apple?**

Finding half a maggot!

••••••••••••••••••

**Why did the baker have smelly hands?**

Because he kneaded a poo.

# TONGUE TWISTERS

Children cannot resist the challenge of a tortuous tongue twister. Hang on! That almost sounds like a tongue twister itself! Tongue twisters are useful to slow kids down and focus them on a simple practical exercise. They sometimes look easy but often turn out to be fiendishly difficult. And then your grandchild will be hooked on the exhausting process of mastering phrases that are likely to tie the inside of their mouth in knots. Challenge the grandkids to see how many times they can say a tongue twister in quick succession without getting it wrong – or how many times they can say it in a minute without completely losing the power of speech! But do be careful if you try to demonstrate the tongue twisters yourself in case you send your dentures flying across the room like a small teeth-shaped Frisbee! Maybe start them off with some simple short traditional tongue twisters, such as:

Round and round the rugged rock the ragged rascal ran.

Red lorry, yellow lorry.

I scream, you scream, we all scream for ice cream!

The sixth sheikh's sixth sheep's sick.

Ken Dodd's dad's dog's dead.

Peggy Babcock.

We surely shall see the sun shine soon.

I wish to wash my Irish wristwatch.

The soldier's shoulder surely hurts.

Three short sword sheaths.

Black background, brown background.

That bloke's back bike brake block broke.

And then of course you can move on to the famous epic poems of the genre:

Peter Piper picked a peck
of pickled peppers.

A peck of pickled peppers
Peter Piper picked.

If Peter Piper picked a peck
of pickled peppers,

Where's the peck of pickled
peppers Peter Piper picked?

How much wood would a woodchuck
chuck if a woodchuck could chuck wood?

He would chuck, he would,
as much as he could,

And chuck as much wood as
a woodchuck would

If a woodchuck could chuck wood.

• • • • • • • • • • • • • •

Betty Botter bought a bit of butter,
But the butter Betty bought was bitter.
So Betty bought a better bit of butter,
Which was better than the bit of butter
Betty bought before.

• • • • • • • • • • • • • •

A Tudor who tooted a flute

Tried to tutor two tooters to toot.

Said the two to their tutor,

'Is it harder to toot

Or to tutor two tooters to toot?'

She sells seashells on the seashore.

The shells she sells are surely seashells.

So if she sells shells on the seashore,

I'm sure she sells seashore shells.

•••••••••••••••

A flea and a fly flew up in a flue.

Said the flea, 'Let us fly!'

Said the fly, 'Let us flee!'

So they flew through a flaw in the flue.

•••••••••••••••

Theophilus Thistle,

The successful thistle sifter,

In sifting a sieve full of unsifted thistles

Thrust three thousand thistles through the thick of his thumb.

# SHAGGY DOG STORIES

As a shaggy dog story is one that is long, pointless and slightly annoying you could always simply relate your entire life story in weekly instalments – but that would be too cruel.

No, let's set some rules here so that you don't drive them (and even yourself) to distraction. How about a story that lasts roughly five minutes and has enough detail to keep them on the edges of their high-chairs, car booster seats or sofas before you deliver the final denouement to general groans?

It has been said that the original shaggy dog story was about someone who owns a shaggy dog and everyone remarks on how remarkably shaggy it is. The owner is so proud of owning such a shaggy dog that he enters it into a shaggy dog competition only to be told, 'Actually, your dog isn't very shaggy at all, is he?'

You will note that we have spared you the full version of this which could run to several minutes, hours or even days if you wished it to, with deviations regarding other, less shaggy dogs, the jealousy of other dog owners, the dog's huge popularity on social media and so on.

So, there you have it – it is in your hands. What's that? You want some suggestions? Oh dear, do we have to do everything for you? Oh, all right then, how about these:

## The Boy With The Magic Puppy

*(Two for the price of one here. Kids like stories that star kids and they also like stories with animals.)*

Once upon a time there was a boy with a magic puppy. He was so magic he could not only play dead, fetch a stick *(feel free to extend this list indefinitely!)* he could do card tricks, juggle balls and plates *(ditto)*, and one day a man called at the boy's house and said, 'I have got a big talent show on TV and I want your puppy to take part. I'm going to make him a star!' So the puppy went on the show and became a huge star and made lots of money and moved to Hollywood, where he lived in a golden kennel and was waited on by servants night and day *(embellish all this as you see fit)* but then, one day, all of a sudden, he wasn't a magic puppy any more. And you know why? Because he'd grown into a magic dog!

## The Multicoloured Fish

Once upon a time there was a multicoloured fish who lived in a multicoloured sea. The fish was red, blue, pink, yellow, purple, puce, heliotrope, silver… (*here you can indulge yourself for a couple of minutes with every exotic colour you can think of*). Every fisherman who ever wanted to fish in the multicoloured sea wanted to catch the multicoloured fish. There was fisherman Fred, fisherman Phil, fisherman Ferdinand… (*well, you're getting the picture now, aren't you?*) and they went out fishing on Mondays, they went out fishing on Tuesdays… they went out fishing on Pancake Day, they went out fishing on… (*carry on as long as you like! After a few minutes of this with variations of your own you need an ending. How about this:*) but no one ever caught the multicoloured fish. And do you know why? Because he lived in a multicoloured sea and no one could see him!

See, now you've got the hang of it you can make up your own shaggy dog stories. If you're stuck for inspiration, here are a few titles that might get you started:

- The whale who ate everything
- The centipede with a sprained ankle
- The gorilla who didn't like bananas
- The rocket ship that wouldn't stop
- The girl who became a millionaire
- The biggest sweet shop in the world
- The bounciest football ever
- The boy with 47 brothers
- The world's biggest pizza
- Jenny's talking cat

# HOW TO MAKE UP JOKES FOR KIDS

There are only so many joke books you can buy, so at some point you might have to start making up your own jokes. We know, you're already an unpaid babysitter, cook, waiter, childminder, teacher, social worker, magician, playgroup leader and storyteller, but you obviously didn't read the job description when you signed up to be a grandparent, did you? It also includes being a stand-up comedian.

Never mind, help is at hand. The easiest jokes in the world to make up are punny jokes. Very punny! See, there's your first one. Find a word with more than one meaning – sack, for example. It could mean a big bag or it could mean getting fired from a job, so you could make a joke saying, 'Why didn't the postman like his job? Because he got the sack every day.'

But you need to be a bit more child-friendly as young kids wouldn't know what getting the sack meant. So think of words that might appeal to children. How about tail/tale? What did Tinkerbell have growing out of her back? A fairy tail.

OK, we never said this was going to be award-winning stuff, but if it keeps them amused for a few minutes you can swallow your pride. (There's probably a granddad beer-drinking pun in there somewhere!)

Of course, anything that's a little bit rude will probably appeal, so you could have something like: Why was the table embarrassed? Because it saw the bottom of the cup.

The other thing is to take a well-known format, say the knock-knock joke, and invent your own. Again, the pun is your best friend.

**Knock, knock.**

Who's there?

**Doctor.**

Doctor who?

**Yes, that's right.**

•••••••••••••••••

**Knock, knock.**

Who's there?

**Ellie.**

Ellie who?

**Elephant.**

Comedy scriptwriters everywhere will at this point be sleeping soundly in their beds knowing that you are not going to steal their livelihood anytime soon, but then your expert cooking of fish fingers, smiley potatoes or fairy cakes will probably not be causing Gordon Ramsay any sleepless nights either. But that's not the point. The fact that you are clever enough to make up your own jokes will secretly impress your lovely grandchildren.

Another format you can use is the 'Why did the chicken cross the road?' one, or 'What do you get if you cross an X with a Y?' Again, those puns are like comedy manna from heaven.

### Why did the skater cross the road?

To get to the other slide.

•••••••••••••••••••

### What do you get if you cross rotten cabbage with a remote control?

Smellyvision.

Or you can just use your punning skills to make up a 'proper' joke:

### What do chickens use to wake up in the morning?

An alarm cluck.

**What's the new social-networking site for grandmas called?**

Instagran!

•••••••••••••••••

**What swims in the sea and tastes of strawberries?**

A jellyfish.

•••••••••••••••••

**What roars and walks funny?**

A bandy lion.

So, the floor is yours. Stick to a format, make the subject matter child-friendly and have fun. And if you think the jokes you make up are bad, just wait until Christmas and see those cracker jokes. The people who write those get paid for it!

Oh, and if you really can't get to grips with the jokes, a funny face or a funny voice will always go down well.

# HOW TO MAKE UP NONSENSICAL STORIES FOR KIDS USING YOUR OWN LIFE

It may well be the case that you don't have to make anything up. Your fantastical tales of having to go to a box at the corner of the street in order to make a phone call will be utterly bizarre to your grandchildren, if not completely unbelievable.

They will also be bemused to learn that instead of downloading or streaming music you went to a place called a 'record shop' to buy a piece of black vinyl, and that you could hear it beforehand in a 'listening booth'.

Similarly, any young teenage grandchildren will be flabbergasted to hear that you found boyfriends and girlfriends through actually going out and meeting them face to face, and no – it wasn't called 'face time'.

They will be astounded to learn that when you did your homework you had to go to a bookshelf or to the library and look at books if you wanted information, and that the internet DID. NOT. EXIST! Shock horror! The internet didn't exist? What?!

Also, when you took pictures you had to use an old-fashioned device called a 'camera' because mobile phones didn't exist. 'So you're telling me the internet didn't exist and mobile phones didn't exist? How? How could you live a normal life?'

You may also be old enough to tell them with a completely straight face that your normal diet did not consist of pizza and hamburgers and was more likely to be toad-in-the-hole and spotted dick. If you're really old you might even have to break the news that at one time crisps didn't come in different flavours – just potato-flavoured, with a little blue bag of salt if you were lucky.

It may also be stretching their credulity to impart the news that when you were a child jeans were not the staple mode of dress for everyone. Boys probably wore grey flannel shorts and girls had flowery dresses, and adults wore proper grown-up clothes like suits and twinsets.

You may be able to tell them that you didn't go abroad until you were an adult, or theme parks didn't exist, or sometimes you used to see policemen walking round the streets, or you had only two or three channels on your TV and even then they were in black and white.

You can paint idyllic pictures of high streets with shops called 'greengrocers' and 'butchers' and 'bakers' and streets with no yellow lines or road humps. You can add that the rag-and-bone man who used to call wasn't a pop star but a bloke with a horse and cart collecting rubbish.

You could even scare the life out of them by recalling that your house was a permanent fug of cigarette smoke due to everyone, including your older siblings, reaching for the gaspers every few minutes.

But perhaps all this is just so, so fantastical that they'd never believe a word of it. And if you mentioned that your pocket money was 10p a week, or that your parents had to buy a licence to keep a dog, or that cinemas only had one screen with about 2,000 people watching it, or that you never went to university (and that even the people who did got paid to go there by the government), they would speak to their parents about getting your medication changed.

No, it's hardly necessary to make up weird and wonderful tales about your life because the reality was far, far weirder and they won't believe a word of it. Perhaps, then, you should concentrate your efforts on weaving tales of dragons and leprechauns, of nine-headed hydras, enchanted forests, giants and monsters, because frankly they might at least find some of that feasible.

## LOGIC PROBLEMS AND PUZZLES TO KEEP THE KIDS FLUMMOXED FOR HOURS

If you want the little darlings to pipe down for a few minutes, why not try giving them a fiendish brain teaser to occupy their grey matter? Hopefully this will keep their brains so busy that all their other functions will be temporarily disabled. They will (at least theoretically) have to sit quietly puzzling over your conundrum for several hours. They may, however, persist in bothering you with cries to 'Give us a clue' or (in the case of grandchildren who may need to develop their powers of concentration a little more) pained sobs of 'Just tell us the answer please!'

Here, then, is a selection of well-known logic problems to try on your grandkids. Remember – don't give them the answers straight away – let them puzzle them out for as long as possible! And, even more importantly, keep this book with the answers well hidden!

### What starts with a T, ends with a T and has T in it?

A teapot.

●●●●●●●●●●●●●●●●

### What gets wetter as it dries?

A towel.

**Is it legal for a man to marry
his widow's sister?**

Certainly not – he's dead
(that's why his wife is a widow)!

•••••••••••••••••

**When is it unlucky to see a black cat?**

When you are a mouse.

•••••••••••••••••

**What has a neck but cannot swallow?**

A bottle.

•••••••••••••••••

**How do you make seven even?**

Take the 's' off it.

•••••••••••••••••

**What do you find at the
end of a rainbow?**

The letter 'w'.

**What occurs once in every minute, twice in every moment, yet never in a thousand years?**

The letter 'm'.

•••••••••••••••

**Which word is always spelled incorrectly?**

Incorrectly.

•••••••••••••••

**To what question can no one ever truthfully give the answer 'Yes'?**

'Are you asleep?'

•••••••••••••••

**Which weighs more – a ton of feathers or a ton of bricks?**

They both weigh exactly the same – one ton to be precise!

**Some months have 31 days in them,
others have 30, but how many have 28?**

All months have 28 days in them – some
just have a few more as well!

•••••••••••••••••

**How far will a blind man
walk into a forest?**

Halfway – after that he will be
walking out of the forest.

•••••••••••••••••

**A man digs a hole 3 feet by 3 feet by
3 feet. How much earth is in it?**

None – it's a hole!

•••••••••••••••••

**Which ancient invention is still in use
in many parts of the world today and
allows people to see through walls?**

A window!

**Four big men have only one tiny umbrella to huddle beneath, but none of them gets wet. Why not?**

It's not raining!

•••••••••••••••

**Which five-letter word becomes shorter when you add two letters to it?**

Short!

•••••••••••••••

**How can you throw a ball as hard as you can, and make it stop and come back to you, without it hitting anything and with nothing attached to it?**

Throw it straight up in the air – gravity will do the rest!

•••••••••••••••

**How can you carry water in a bucket full of holes?**

Freeze the water solid first.

**Where does Friday come before Thursday?**

In a dictionary.

••••••••••••••••••

**Three men all fall in the sea but only one gets his hair wet. Why?**

The other two are bald!

••••••••••••••••••

**A plane crashes exactly on the border between Italy and Switzerland. Where do they bury the survivors?**

Nowhere – you don't bury the survivors!

There are also of course some great traditional logic problems which are more epic in their narrative extent, locations and range of characters!

**Two fathers and two sons go out for a day's fishing. Each of them catches a fish. When they get home there are three fish. How is this possible? And no – they didn't lose or eat any of the fish on the way back!**

The fishermen were a man, his father and his son – so there were two fathers and two sons but only three people!

•••••••••••••••••••

**A man builds a rectangular house. Every window on every side of the house has a view looking south. One day the man looks out of one of the windows and sees a bear. What colour is the bear?**

The bear is white – it's a polar bear. If every window in his house looks south, he must be at the North Pole – although admittedly this is an unusual location for a real estate project and probably not conveniently situated for any local amenities.

You are alone in a completely deserted
house at night and it's pitch black.
All you have is an oil lamp, a candle,
firewood and just one match.
Which is it best to light first?

The match!

••••••••••••••••

A man is looking at a photograph
and declares of the person depicted,
'Brothers and sisters I have none, but
this man's father is my father's son.'
Who is the person in the photo?

The man's son!

••••••••••••••••

A man walks into a bar. He asks
the barman for a glass of water. Instead
the barman pulls out a gun and points
it at him. The man thanks the barman
and walks back out of the bar.
What was going on?

The man had hiccups. He asked the
barman for some water to help cure his
hiccups. Instead the barman pulled out
a gun. The shock was sufficient to stop
the hiccups. And so the man was grateful
and left. However, this is not a safe,
recommended cure for hiccups.

A window cleaner is cleaning the windows on the thirtieth floor of a huge apartment block in the middle of a big city. Suddenly the window cleaner slips and falls to the ground. He had not been wearing any safety harness or other equipment. And yet he walks away completely unscathed. How?

He was cleaning the windows inside the apartment!

••••••••••••••••

A woman has two sons born at the same time on the same day of the same month in the same year. But they are not twins. Why not?

They're triplets – there's another one of them somewhere!

••••••••••••••••

You have two strings of different lengths and some matches. The longer string will burn for exactly ten minutes if you light one end of it. The shorter string will burn for exactly one minute. How do you use your two pieces of string to time exactly five minutes and 30 seconds?

Take your longer string and fold it exactly in half. Light both ends. It will take exactly five minutes for both of the halves to burn. Then do the same with the shorter string. It will take exactly 30 seconds for the two halves of this to burn.

**You have six glasses lined up as shown,
with three containing orange juice and
three empty. How can you make the glasses
alternate between full and empty glasses by
moving only one of the glasses?**

Pick up the second of the full glasses and pour
the contents into the second of the empty glasses.

•••••••••••••••••

**A man is travelling with a fox, a goose and
a sack of corn. Don't ask why – he just likes
travelling around with these three things.**

**The man reaches a river and has to cross it.
He finds a boat which he can use but the boat
is only big enough to fit himself and either
the fox, the goose or the corn. So he can only
carry one of them across at a time.**

**He can't leave the fox with the goose
because the fox will eat the goose. And he
can't leave the goose with the corn because
the goose will eat the corn.**

**How does the man manage to get
himself and his fox, goose and corn across
the river without any of them being left
somewhere they will get eaten?**

The answer is that he takes the goose over first, leaves it and comes back. He then takes the fox over and brings the goose back. Next he takes the corn across and leaves that with the fox. Finally he goes back and gets the goose. This goose has managed to get three trips in the boat and the fox and the corn only got one! And what's more, couldn't he have got the goose to swim across to save a couple of trips?

••••••••••••••••••

**A man dies and is on his way to heaven. He finds himself faced with two doors. One leads to heaven and the other directly to the fires of hell. But he cannot tell which door is which. There are two guards, one by each door. One always tells the truth; the other always lies. What question does the man ask to find out for certain which door will take him to heaven and which to hell?**

The answer is that the man says to one of the guards: 'If I asked the other guard, 'Which door leads to Heaven?' what would he tell me?' The truth-telling guard would truthfully say that the other guard would tell him the wrong door while the lying guard would lie and say that the other guard would tell him the wrong door. So, whichever guard he asks, he will be told which is the wrong door!

●●●●●●●●●●●●●●●●●

**A man lives on the tenth floor of an apartment building. Every morning he goes to the lift and rides down to the ground floor. When he comes back if there is someone else in the lift he will go back to his floor directly. If there isn't anyone in the lift, he goes up to the seventh floor and walks up the stairs back to his apartment on the tenth floor. Why?**

The answer is that the man is a very short, tiny person who is unable to reach the button for the tenth floor on his own. But if that's the case why did this man move into an apartment that was so difficult to access in the first place?!

## THE CHARACTERISTICS OF FUN AND NOT-SO-FUN GRANDPARENTS

You may remember the characteristics of your own grandparents, and if you were lucky you had two sets of each. Did you have one granddad who was always telling jokes and doing tricks and another one who sat grumpily in his armchair telling you to shush while he read the paper? Did you have one granny who had rosy cheeks and smelled of home-baking and another one with thin lips who smelled of mothballs?

Which will you be?

Of course, in today's world kids might have one granddad who still wears a leather jacket and plays electric guitar and one who wears a threadbare cardigan and collects old bus tickets. They might have one granny who has a 500-cc motorbike and one who makes patchwork quilts.

But whichever type you are, you can still be a fun grandparent. It's all a case of knowing what kids will find appealing. Part of this is becoming a kid again yourself (while still having a bit of grandparental authority, of course – 'Don't play with your food!').

It might have been 20 or 30 years since your kids were kids, so you may be a bit out of practice at playing 'catch', blowing a bubblegum bubble or remembering the words to 'Incy Wincy Spider', but it will all come back to you, promise! In the meantime, check the following table for pointers:

| Fun grandparents | Not-so-fun grandparents |
|---|---|
| Will have a go on the slide in the playground. | Will have a go at the other kids in the playground. |
| Will make rude noises with the aid of a deflating balloon. | Will make rude noises towards any kid who tries it. |
| Will teach the kids how to make fairy cakes. | Will teach the kids how to file a tax return. |
| Will let them do something a bit messy like painting. | Will get them to redecorate their living room for them. |

# TO BRIBE OR NOT TO BRIBE

Whisper it softly, but kids are a mercenary lot. Show us a kid who won't change their mind about tidying their toys away when there's 50p or a chocolate biscuit in it and we'll show you a kid who has yet to learn the subtle art of negotiation.

And you grandparents have probably got plenty of experience yourselves, going back to your own childhood demands for half a crown or a groat or two for fetching your parents' cigarettes, or your own children's demands to be paid for walking the family dog or tidying their bedrooms.

Yes, nothing has changed much over the years, apart from inflation which means by the time your grandchildren are teenagers they will only be interested in paper money and not coins. Shocking to find that bribing a kid in the twenty-first century might set you back the equivalent of what you used to get paid for a week's work back in the day.

Perhaps the following could serve as an indication of when to bribe and when not to bribe (but whatever you do, don't call it a bribe – it's an advance reward for good behaviour):

| Do bribe when... | Don't bribe when... |
| --- | --- |
| You have tried sweet reason and it has failed. | You have tried sweets and they now want hard cash. |
| You have several more hours of babysitting ahead and it will be worth every penny. | There's only half an hour till the parents get back and you can threaten their imminent ire instead. |
| Not bribing will be more expensive – e.g. when they are just about to set fire to your curtains. | They have already set fire to your curtains. They now have to bribe you in exchange for not telling their parents. |
| The grandchildren are very young and a lovely silver 5p will be riches indeed. | They're 15 and are expecting a bank transfer. |

# SURE–FIRE WAYS TO GET KIDS' ATTENTION

The attention span of kids, especially young ones, is probably even shorter than your own. What's that? You weren't listening? We were talking about attention spans; now try to keep up.

What is an attention span? It's the amount of time someone can stay focused on one thing before being distracted by something else. So at school, for example, the distraction of a fight breaking out in the playground, seen through the class window, is instantly more attention-grabbing than the characteristics of equilateral triangles. In fact, for most schoolchildren finding the tipping point of a ruler on the edge of their desk is also more interesting than the characteristics of equilateral triangles. As is watching a fly walking up the wall or counting the ceiling tiles.

And there you have it. If you lumber kids with something they perceive as being boring (some mathematicians, of course, would find equilateral triangles pretty exciting stuff) then anything, anything at all, will be more interesting.

Your task then is to never let them get bored. But how?

**Rule number one:** get them doing stuff rather than listening to you. Riveting though your story about queuing at the post office might be to a septuagenarian, it might be less so to a five-year-old. So always have pens, paper, glue, scissors and other goodies to hand for them to play with (health and safety alert on scissors notwithstanding).

**Rule number two:** turn boring things into a game. Rather than saying, 'Who's going to help me tidy up?' say, 'Right, first one to collect ten pieces of paper off the floor is the winner!'

**Rule number three:** kids march on their stomachs, so always have a supply of snacks at the ready. These can also be used as rewards, bribes, prizes, etc. Do try and lay off the E-numbers, though, as there's only one thing worse than a fractious child and that's a hyper-fractious child who's just gorged to the gills on sugar-coated E-numbers!

**Rule number four:** the mystery police. The mystery police are any unseen eyes that are watching what the kids are getting up to – and not approving, of course. 'What would your mum say if she saw you doing that?' 'What would your teacher say…?' and so on. You can even enlist the assistance of dolls, teddy bears and other anthropomorphic creatures. 'Look, Teddy's sad that you're behaving like that…'

**Rule number five:** harness their natural competitiveness. Whether we like it or not kids are competitive – they wouldn't have any truck with those games where there aren't any winners. So, competitions about who can sit up straightest, who can stay quiet longest, who can eat everything on their plate (and so on) get them to do what you want while satisfying their natural desire to compete. Everyone's a winner – or possibly not!

**Rule number six:** appeal to their egos. This is related to rule number five. Asking 'Now, who is really clever…?' will have them all jumping up and down and saying 'Me! Me!' though the enthusiasm may suddenly wear off if you complete the sentence with '… at laying the table?'

**Last-ditch attempts:** if all else fails, the following are pretty much guaranteed to get kids' attention:

- Who likes ice cream?

- Who wants to earn some money?

- Who wants to go to the swings?

- Who likes chocolate?

Warning: these are only to be used in emergencies, as once you have used them you have nowhere else to go that will be more interesting/appealing/exciting. Even the promise of one of your best magic tricks or knock-knock jokes will have difficulty in competing with these.

# TRICKS TO BAFFLE, IMPRESS AND/OR TEACH TO KIDS

As we've mentioned, as a grandparent you now have a multitude of different hats to wear, so why not a black pointy one with stars all over it? All right, you're not going to become Gandalf or Professor Dumbledore, but you could become a slightly wrinkled Derren Brown, albeit without all the razzmatazz.

Yes, you are going to become a magician! What's that – the only trick you know is how to make a gin and tonic disappear? Never mind, help is at hand.

A lot will depend, of course, on the ages of the grandchildren you are looking after. An impromptu pulling of a sweet from behind the ear of a five-year-old might not be quite so thrilling for a bright 13-year-old who will note that it was in your hand all along.

So what you need is a range of tricks from which you can select ones to suit your audience, and you won't need any special equipment, rabbits or live doves. Just a pack of cards, a few coins and general bits and bobs that you have lying round the house.

You could even teach some of the tricks to the kids for them to impress their friends with. And the good news is that, as you are probably not a member of the Magic Circle, you can't very well be thrown out for revealing 'how it's done'.

If you really want to go the full monty, you could invest in a black cape and a magic wand but it's up to you. And if your other half is around they can be your 'glamorous assistant'.

So, what are you waiting for? Let the magic commence!

# TRICKS WITH MATCHSTICKS

Who could forget the classic brain teasers that can be conjured up just by whipping a box of matches out of your pocket?

OK, the first problem with doing them today is probably going to be the fact that you no longer have any reason to use matches! Your cooker lights itself, your heating switches itself on and, even if the stresses of looking after your grandchildren might cause you to look back fondly to the days when you smoked like a chimney, now is no time to take the filthy habit up again.

Hopefully, however, you will be able to find a box of matches somewhere at the back of a cupboard and be able to use these to teach the kids these traditional old tricks.

Do not of course leave the grandchildren for a moment to play with the matches unsupervised. In fact, these days there is probably a health and safety poster you should stick up on the wall whenever matches are being used to alert all present to the dangers involved.

Maybe it would be best to look online for a pack of special non-flammable matchsticks to help you perform the following puzzles and tricks. Or of course cocktail sticks may provide a suitable replacement (if the pointy ends don't also get you in trouble with the health and safety people).

## Turn Two Squares into Three Squares

Lay out the matches as below and ask the grandchildren if they can make three squares out of the arrangement by moving only four of the matches!

After they've spent a few hours puzzling over that one, you can show them the answer which is to rearrange two matches from each of two opposite corners:

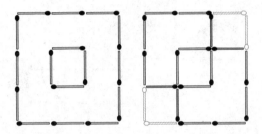

## Turn a Noughts and Crosses Grid into Three Squares

Make a Noughts-and-Crosses-style grid with your matches and ask the grandchildren if they can turn this configuration into three complete squares by moving just three matches.

After another few hours of peace and quiet you can show them the answer, which is to move three matches from one side and use them to complete the remaining squares like so:

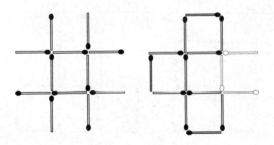

## Turn Five Squares into Four

Make five squares with your matchsticks (as shown below left) and ask the kids to turn them into four by moving just two matches.

The solution is achieved by moving a match from the top and another from the bottom to form a new square at the top:

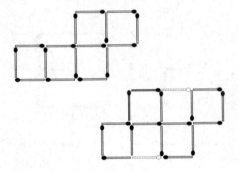

## Turn Four Squares into Three

This time, make four squares and ask the grandchildren if they can turn the arrangement into three squares by moving just three matchsticks.

The way to do this is to take the two matchsticks from the top left corner and the one from the bottom right edge and use these to create a square with the remaining matchstick on the bottom right.

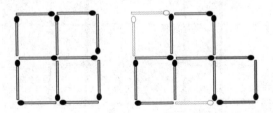

## Make the Matchsticks Switch Direction

Lay out ten matchsticks in columns of descending size, as shown below. Now challenge the grandchildren to move just three matchsticks and reverse the direction of the arrangement (so the column with four matchsticks is on the extreme right and the single matchstick is on the extreme left).

The solution involves taking the single matchstick from the extreme right and moving it to the extreme left while taking two matchsticks from the column of four on the extreme left and adding these to the column of two.

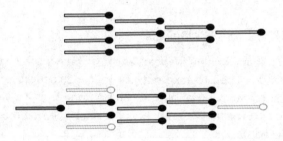

## Turn Eleven Matchsticks into Nine

Lay out 12 matchsticks any old how. Now ask the grandchildren if they can take one away and leave nine. This should keep them quiet for hours until you demonstrate the solution, which involves arranging the remaining 11 matchsticks as below. Prepare yourself for the sound of anguished groaning and noisome complaints from the grandchildren!

## Turn Six Squares into Three

Lay out your matchsticks as below left and ask the grandchildren to take away six matchsticks to leave only three squares. The matchsticks to remove are shown below right.

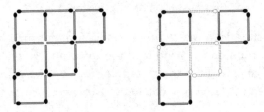

## Turn Nine Triangles into Six

Create a shape of nine triangles as shown below and challenge the grandchildren to take out just four matchsticks and turn the design into six triangles. It can be done by removing the two matchsticks at the apex plus the next one down on each outside edge:

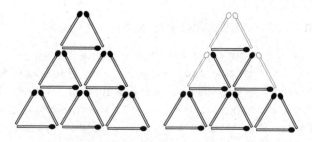

## Turn Three Triangles into Two

Ask your grandchildren if they can move two matchsticks in the arrangement below left to make one big triangle and one smaller triangle.

The answer is to take the two matchsticks from the middle and move them to form the apex of a larger triangle. You now have one large triangle and one smaller triangle formed at its apex.

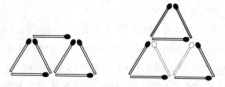

## Turn Nine Squares into Five

Ask the grandchildren if they can take eight matchsticks from this arrangement and leave only five squares.

The answer is to take away the two matchsticks that form each corner leaving only the five squares formed in the centre.

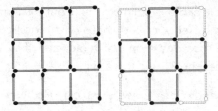

## Make Six Matchsticks Touch Each Other

Simply set out six matchsticks and ask the grandchildren if they can arrange them so each one of the matchsticks is touching every other one.

The solution may astonish, amaze and very possibly provoke further cries of anguish!

# COIN TRICKS

Of course, the main trick for many people of advancing years will be to have any money in the first place! But when you do happen to have any, squirrel away a few coins of different denominations and you will have the essential props for lots of different magic tricks. No special skills are required, just maybe a bit of practice in front of a mirror. If you can fool yourself you can fool anyone!

## The Disappearing Pound

Put a 2p piece on your left palm just below your third and fourth fingers, and a £1 coin on your right palm near the base of your thumb. Tell your audience you are going to turn your hands over, face down on the table, and they have to say which one has the £1 underneath it.

With your hands close together quickly flip them over flat on the table and the £1 coin should travel across to now be under your left hand. The children will remember that the £1 coin was in your right hand so will assume it is under there. You, however, can turn the right palm over to reveal that the £1 has disappeared and then you can turn your left palm over to reveal that both coins are under there.

With a bit of practice, you can do a variation on this trick and put each coin near the base of the thumb on each hand so that when you flip your palms over each of the coins will switch to the other hand.

## Nothing Up My Sleeves!

On no account should you utter the above phrase because that's exactly where your coin will be! Drop a coin down your sleeve (a loose long-sleeved shirt) while your arm is bent at the elbow. The coin should then lodge there until such time as you want to make it magically appear simply by straightening your arm downwards with your cupped hand waiting to catch it. Using this simple trick you can now build up to it by showing your empty palms, using some magic words and then making the coin magically appear in your hand.

## The Coin from Nowhere

This is a very simple trick that may need a bit of practice, but can be very effective. Put a coin between the two middle fingers of your right hand so that it is protruding from the back of your hand. Show your palms to the audience which will appear to be empty. Then, perhaps using a few magic words or a bit of patter cross your hands over each other several times while dropping the coin into your left hand and making fists of both hands. You can then reveal that a coin has magically appeared from nowhere!

# SECRET CIPHERS, CODES AND CODEBREAKING

The use of secret codes and ciphers may also keep the grand offspring occupied for a little while. Kids may enjoy ciphers and codes because of the element of secrecy involved. This is despite the fact that the use of codes and ciphers can be quite time-consuming and it can therefore take several hours to pass one simple short message to someone sitting in the same room not far away from yourself.

If you're lucky, then, you could occupy your grandchildren for an entire afternoon in the effort of coding and decoding a message which turns out to be telling them what's for dinner that evening.

Obviously, any codes, ciphers or elements of cryptography to which you introduce your grandchildren should be relatively simple. There's no use trying to get them to crack the Enigma code at this stage. So as you work your way up to that, hopefully they will find the following beginner's guide to code making and breaking fun and inspiring.

## Reverse Alphabet

A reverse-alphabet cipher is precisely that. Simply write out the alphabet and underneath it write the alphabet in reverse. In other words A=Z, B=Y, C=X and so on. Then your grandchildren can write secret messages using this system, convinced that you will never be able to decipher them – even though you were the one who just taught them how to do it.

## Using a Book as a Cipher

Messages can be created and deciphered using a number code referring to different words in a printed book. For example, 3967 would refer to the ninth word on the third line of page 67. Go through the book and find enough words to create a coded message using this system.

For this method you should have two completely identical copies of the same book. Perhaps your grandchildren will have a favourite book in their house and you have a spare copy in yours.

Or, of course, after creating your coded message you can simply hand your grandchildren the book you just used, which they can now use to decipher what you said!

Don't forget, however, to choose a book that has lots of different words in it. If the book you choose is an early reader's title with only one word on each page, your messages will have to be quite simple!

## Invisible Ink

These days you will probably be able to find all sorts of invisible writing pens and kits to buy, but don't forget good old-fashioned lemon juice! Simply squeeze a bit of lemon juice and mix with a bit of water. Messages can then be written on paper using a cotton bud dipped into the watered juice. Once dry the message should be completely invisible (if you don't look too closely).

In order to reveal the message, heat the paper by holding it near to a light bulb. If this doesn't work because the light bulbs in your house are all too energy efficient, you may have to resort to holding the paper near a lit candle.

Obviously careful supervision should be exercised when doing this, so ask your grandchildren to watch very carefully in case your shaky old hands cause the paper to catch light and burn your house down.

## Banana Writing

Another way to pass on secret messages is via the medium of bananas. OK, it's not a system often used by the secret service or in James Bond films, but it does work! First, find a nice fresh yellowy banana and a cocktail stick which can be used to gently etch a short message on the skin of the banana such as, 'Hello!', or your name or 'Don't forget to eat this banana!'

At first the message will be invisible, but after an hour it will turn brown and should be easily legible. Once the message has been read, get the kids to destroy the evidence by eating the banana and disposing of the skin in the bin (or composter).

Do not encourage them to use the banana skin for any further espionage activities, for example, by throwing it on the pavement outside your house in an attempt to make passing enemy agents slip up!

## MAGICAL TRICKS WITH NUMBERS (WARNING – CONTAINS NO ACTUAL MAGIC!)

If you have young and impressionable grandchildren, it is possible they will believe you are able to read and control minds even if they are aware that you have trouble just getting your mobile phone to work.

Number-based tricks may be a useful way to convince the grandkids that you have magical psychic powers. Often they will get so bamboozled by the prospect of having to do maths when it's not even homework that they will find it easier to believe that you are able to see into their brains (rather than having cheated by using a few simple bits of arithmetic).

Try some of the following and then, after a couple of minutes basking in your grandchildren's admiration of your supernatural abilities, you can teach them how to do the same tricks on their friends!

## Three Digits

Ask your grandchild to think of a three-digit number in which the digits are all different (e.g. 547). Or if you have multiple grandchildren ask them each for a number between one and ten until you have your three digits.

Now get your grandchild to write the three digits down on a piece of paper and then to write down the digits in reverse immediately underneath. Ask them to subtract whichever is the lower number from whichever is the higher (e.g. 745 – 547 = 198). Take the result and write this in reverse immediately underneath. So if you had ended up with 198, write 891 beneath.

Now add the two numbers together (so for example, 891 + 198 = 1,089). If for some ungodly reason you end up at any stage with a number which has only two digits, put a zero in front of it to make it three digits (e.g. 312 – 213 = 99; 099 + 990 = 1,089).

As you may now have begun to notice, the result of this messing around is always 1,089. You can either prove your magical powers to your grandchild by having the number written ready on a piece of paper which you reveal when they've done their sums…

… or – even more magically – you can refer them to a book on the bookshelf and get them to look up the page indicated by the first three numbers (108) and then count to the ninth word on the page (which you will have already memorised and so been able to predict).

If, however, they end up with a different answer, you may have to get out your pocket calculator and let them use this as you repeat the entire exercise!

## The Magic Vegetable

Write down the word 'carrot' on a piece of paper and keep it hidden. Then ask your grandchild to do the following sums in order: 'What's 1 + 1? What's 2 + 2? What's 4 + 4? What's 8 + 8?' Then ask them to name a vegetable. People usually answer 'carrot'.

If they do so, you can reveal your piece of paper with the word 'carrot' written on it and receive their admiration and applause. If they name another vegetable, don't show them the piece of paper! You should instead conclude the trick by saying 'I knew you were going to say that!' which is slightly less impressive but may be the best you can do in the circumstances.

If you have very small children who answer by saying something like 'a banana' or 'oven chips' or 'pickled onion Monster Munch', you can take the opportunity to have a discussion with them about what a vegetable is!

## Age–Related Magic 1

Ask your grandchild to multiply the first number of their age by 5. Now ask them to take this number and add 3 to it. Get them to double this answer. Now ask them to add on the second number of their age. Finally ask them to tell you the answer they have ended up with. If you take away 6 from this answer, you will have their age. But it's your grandchild – so you'll probably already know how old they are! Also your grandchildren may be aged under 10 in which case you will have to take the first number of their age as being zero!

## Age–Related Magic 2

Ask your grandchild which month of the year they were born and which number corresponds to it (i.e. January is 1, February 2, March 3, etc.).

Then (and maybe offer them a calculator at this point) ask them to add 18 to this number, then multiply the answer by 25, take away 333 from the result, multiply this answer by 8, subtract 554, divide by 2, add the number of the day of the month they were born, multiply by 5, add 692, multiply by 20, add the last numbers of the year they were born and finally subtract 32,940.

Now tell them to look at the answer. The first one or two digits are the month they were born, the next two are the day they were born and the last two are the year they were born!

## Age–Related Magic 3

A nice simple one! Ask your grandchild to multiply their age by 7 and then multiply the result by 1,443. The answer should be their age repeated three times!

## Age–Related Magic 4

Ask your grandchild to think of a number between 1 and 100 but not to tell you what it is. Pick up a calculator, ask your grandchild their age (you should definitely know what this is by now, but ask them anyway), type this in, multiply it by 2, add 5, multiply the result by 50 and take away 365 from the answer.

Now hand your grandchild the calculator and ask them to add on their secret number (if they can still remember it) without letting you see what it is. Take back the calculator and add 115. With a proud flourish, show your grandchild the answer on the calculator screen.

The first half of the number is their age and the second half is their secret number!

## The Scandinavian Pachyderm Trick

Ask your grandchild to pick a number (any number!) between 1 and 10 and then to multiply this by 9. If the answer is a two-digit number, ask them to add the two digits together and subtract 5 from the result.

Now ask them to count through each letter of the alphabet (i.e. A = 1, B = 2, C = 3, etc.) until they reach the number where they ended up.

Finally ask them to think of a country that begins with the letter they reached, an animal whose name begins with the second letter of the country they just thought of and a colour normally associated with the animal.

Usually the answer will be a grey elephant from Denmark. Although if your grandchildren have spent much time in Djibouti, Dominica, the Dominican Republic, the Democratic Republic of Congo or Democratic People's Republic of Korea, they may give a different answer.

# TRICKS WITH CARDS

If you tell your grandchildren that you're going to show them some card tricks, they may presume that you're about to whip the plastic out of your wallet or purse and buy them a load of goodies online. Or, even better, maybe they'll think you're about to tell them their mum or dad's PIN so they can help themselves to whatever they want.

But of course you are about to demonstrate some good old-fashioned tricks using traditional playing cards. You may be tempted to preface your performance by producing your pack of cards with a flourish and fanning them out before your grandchildren. If you do so, be careful not to immediately destroy the effect by taking over five minutes to shuffle the pack by clumsily stuffing one card at a time into the pack at various angles and occasionally dropping them all over the floor.

## A Simple 'Find the Card' Trick

Have a pack of cards ready before the kids come round and remember which card is on the bottom. When the kids arrive fan the deck of cards out and ask one of them to pick a card and remember it without telling you.

Then cut the pack in two and put their card on top of the half of the deck that was on top. Then put the other half on top of that so the card you memorised from the bottom of the pack is now on top of the card they chose. At this point you can use some stage patter, magic words, etc. and tell them you will find their card which has been 'lost' in the middle of the deck.

Then simply go through the pack, turning over each card in turn and the one immediately after the one you memorised will be their card. Because this is so simple you can show them how to do it – unless you want to retain your mystique!

## Magic Colours

Before the kids arrive, prepare a pack of cards by putting all the red cards on top and all the black cards on the bottom. When the kids are ready, hold the pack up and say you are going to split it into two halves. You should be able to flick through them, glancing at the colours, and split them at the point where the colour changes.

Then pick up one of the piles, fan the cards out and ask one of the kids to pick a card. While he or she is distracted by looking at the card, put the pile back on the table and pick up the other pile and ask them to put the card back in the half pack.

Then put one pile on top of the other and cut the pack once or twice and say you are going to look through and find their card. With the cards facing you, you will easily see that one of them is in the 'wrong' half and be able to identify it as their card.

## The Grandparent of All Card Tricks!

Take 21 cards from a pack and put them in three piles of seven cards face down on the table. Ask a volunteer to pick one of the piles and then fan the cards out facing them and ask them to remember one of the cards but not to tell you what it is.

You then put those seven cards in between the remaining two lots of seven cards so you have a mini-pack of 21 cards. Deal those out one by one into three sets of seven again and ask your volunteer which set their card is in now.

Put that lot of seven in between the other two lots of seven cards again and then deal them out one by one into another three piles of seven. Ask the volunteer which pile their card is in and put that pile in between the other two piles of seven cards.

Then, count out one card for each letter of the word 'grandparent'. When you get to the last letter, 't', you will have found their card! The trick will work just as well if you use any other phrase 11 letters long instead of 'grandparent' – e.g. 'this is yours!' 'smellyphant', 'my schnozzle' or 'oh bumfuzzle!'

## The Next Level

If you start to enjoy this, you could always invest in some of the special packs of cards that are available for budding magicians. For example, you can now buy a pack that contains 52 of the same card, or a marked deck or some other fiendish thing. Just don't be tempted to use them at your next bridge game.

# TRICKS WITH YOUR FINGERS

If you don't have matches, coins or cards to hand, hopefully you still have a full complement of fingers at your disposal. Of course, there are many tricks that grandparents wish they could do using their fingers, such as opening a new jar of marmalade, accurately keying in their PIN or moving their fingers without producing a series of cracking and popping noises that sound like an extended castanet solo. Here, though, are some classic old finger tricks which you can use to impress your grandchildren with a genuinely digital experience.

## Stealing Your Grandchild's Nose

The absolute classic. Practise sticking the tip of your thumb between your first and second fingers so it appears like the end of a nose sticking out from your hand. Then if you pretend to pluck something from the middle of a grandchild's face you can present your fist with the nose apparently protruding between your fingers. At the same time, inform your grandchild that you have had to remove their nose temporarily to examine it and/or give it a good wipe. Don't forget to put the nose back on their face once you've finished. Very small children may check their face to see what has happened to their nose. Others may be less easily fooled.

Please note: no actual noses should be stolen in the course of this trick.

## Finger Calculator

If you have a full quota of ten fingers you can show your grandchildren how to use them as a calculator – albeit one that is only good for multiplying by nine. Hold out your hands side by side with all fingers extended and ask the grandchild to suggest a number between one and ten to be multiplied by nine. The grandchild suggests, for example, 'Four!' Now count your fingers one by one from the left and when you reach your fourth finger hold it down. You should now have three fingers still extended on the left side and six fingers still extended on the right. And indeed 4 × 9 is 36! Try the same method for a different number and as long as no fingers have dropped off, it should work for other multiplications of 9 (up to 9 × 10!).

## Eleven Fingers

Tell your grandchildren you have 11 fingers. Demonstrate this by holding out the fingers of your left hand and touching each of them with your right index finger as you count them – '1, 2, 3, 4, 5'. Then move on to the fingers of your right hand and count these with your left index finger '6, 7, 8, 9, 10'. 'That's funny,' you comment. 'I definitely had 11 before. Let's count them again.' And with incredible sleight of hand, count the fingers on your right hand back down again. '10, 9, 8, 7, 6...' Then hold up your left hand. 'Plus the five on here makes 11!'

# MYSTERIOUS PHYSICAL FORCES

As you will be all too aware, the arrival of grandchildren in your house will unleash many mysterious physical forces. For a start, it may be a mystery to you just how much physical force these small creatures can contain, and it is for this reason that you feel the need to move delicate ornaments and other fragile objects safely out of the way. Some grandparents, of course, place themselves in the fragile objects category and spend the duration of their grandchildren's visit hiding in a darkened wardrobe.

You can, however, try entertaining your grandchildren with a number of traditional little tricks and phenomena that incorporate unexpected bodily reactions. Luckily none of these will involve the unexpected reactions that these days characterise your digestive system.

## Pencil Points

Present your grandchild with two pencils. Tell them to hold one in each hand and to close one of their eyes. Now ask them to try and touch the two pencil points together – which should prove unexpectedly difficult!

## Controlling Fingers with an Invisible Magic Force

Tell your grandchild you can use your telekinetic powers to push their fingers together even when they try to keep them apart. First, ask your grandchild to clasp their hands together tightly and extend their two first fingers. Tell them to hold these fingers up and to keep them apart from one another.

Now hold out one of your fingers or a pencil, or of course your magic wand, and use this to circle through the air around the grandchild's two first fingers. Gradually the grandchild's two fingers will be drawn together despite their best efforts and you imploring them to remember to hold their fingers apart!

## Coloured Colours

You can perform this trick using a sheet of blank paper and a selection of coloured pens. Write down the names of different colours on the paper but for every colour named always use the wrong coloured pen. So for example you might write the word 'red' in green ink, the word 'blue' in brown ink, the word 'yellow' in purple ink and so on.

Now ask your grandchild to name the colours in which each word is written rather than reading the words themselves. Again they should find this quite difficult to do. Unless of course your grandchild is very young and hasn't learnt to read yet!

If your grandchild tells you, 'Granddad/Grandma, this is a well-known scientific phenomenon called the Stroop effect,' then it is becoming clear that they are destined to go far in life!

## Becoming Unable to Pick Up Something Right in Front of You

Ask your grandchild to stand against a wall with their heels touching it (or the skirting board at its base – let's not split hairs here!). Now find something that they might conceivably want to get their hands on (e.g. a banana, their mobile phone or the details of a helpline for those whose grandparents keep doing silly tricks all the time) and place it on the floor in front of them.

Tell your grandchild to lean over and pick this item up without bending their knees or moving their feet. They should find they are unable to perform this simple action! Of course, ageing grandparents may also have difficulty in picking up things that are right in front of them, whether or not they are standing against a wall.

## Floating Arms

Tell your grandchild you can make their arm rise up without them wanting it to. First, tell them to stand pressing the back of one of their hands against a wall. Get them to keep doing this for a full 30 seconds or more.

Now tell them to step away from the wall and let their arm hang loose by their side. Tell them that you will now perform some hocus-pocus and use your telekinetic powers to make their arm rise up in the air whether they want it to or not. And indeed their arm should now mysteriously float up from their side.

For a stereo effect, get a volunteer grandchild to stand in a doorway pressing the backs of both hands against each side of the frame for 30 seconds or more. Then you can use your powers to make both arms float up.

If your grandchild tells you, 'Don't be silly, Granddad/Grandma. This is yet another well-known scientific effect called the Kohnstamm phenomenon!' they will either be a budding scientific genius or have recently learnt about this at school.

# A SHORT GUIDE TO KIDS' ENERGY LEVELS

Kids have two energy levels: high and off the scale. That's all you need to know, really. If you're new to this grandparenting lark it might come as a bit of a shock to find that after a couple of hours running round like maniacs in the park they do not come home and fall asleep on the sofa like you. No, they run around the house like maniacs for another couple of hours.

If you're a grandparent you must of course have had kids of your own and should remember all this, but it was a long, long time ago, plus you were 20 or 30 years younger then and could keep up with it all, but now...?

They say that if you run a marathon you have to pace yourself. You can't dash off the starting line at a sprint pace – you save that for the end. Same with grandparenting. Don't start the day with a mad game of 'chase'; try the gentler pastimes of going to the zoo or having a quiet indoor game. Save the marathon-ending sprint for later.

So whatever you do, don't try to match the energy levels of your grandchildren. You have an ageing body that sends you constant handy reminders to not overdo things. Young children haven't started receiving these messages yet. Essentially this is because they are young and therefore new and their bodies are still in full working order and under guarantee.

Small children have much in common with the earliest moments in the history of the universe. They contain an extraordinary amount of energy held in a very concentrated space which is likely to suddenly burst out in all directions. When they arrive at your house, the release of energy will be akin to that which occurred at the moment of the Big Bang.

Your job is therefore to act like a nuclear scientist. You need to find a way to harness the immense power being unleashed by your grandchildren and direct this to useful, rather than destructive, means. If they are shooting round your house like electrons round a nucleus, then maybe it's time to take them outside to play in the park or just in the back garden or somewhere.

Unlike you, your grandchildren will rarely plonk themselves down on the sofa with a sigh of exhaustion and mild pain. In fact, they will rarely sit down at all. Instead they will keep on running round until they collapse – quite literally – like burnt-out fireworks.

So one essential thing to remember is to be careful in case they reach their collapsing stage at some distant point from your house or car. If this happens, you may find yourself having to carry them back like a sack of potatoes. After this, you will also collapse in a state of exhaustion, probably at the exact moment your grandchildren leap up again miraculously completely revived.

# AN EVEN SHORTER GUIDE TO GRANDPARENTS' ENERGY LEVELS

It may well be the case that the phrase 'grandparents' energy levels' is a contradiction in terms. Do you have any? Well, you might have a smidgen before the grandchildren come round, but afterwards? If you're a grandparent you probably don't have any energy, and if you have any energy you're probably not a grandparent.

And don't forget if your house is suddenly full of grandchildren running around like mad things, it's probably best if you avoid looking at them too closely. As an ageing person, it is possible for you to become physically exhausted not by doing anything yourself, but simply by the act of watching somebody else doing something.

At the same time, of course, you do have to keep an eye on the little ones in case of potential mishaps. Sitting watching the grandchildren run around will, however, count as your exercise for the day.

The secret is not to try to do everything the kids do. If you're a tennis coach, do you sweat it out for four hours using every ounce of your energy? No, you make the player do all the work while you sit on the sidelines offering advice.

So if the kids want to run round the house playing Murder in the Dark, you don't have to do all the running around as well – you can get the biscuits and drinks ready for when they finish, and with a bit of luck they'll be quiet for five minutes then.

If possible, try to direct the children's energy into something which is physically demanding in some way, but which doesn't involve too much supervision. If you can get them to clean your house for you without fear of damage to themselves (or the house), then that's all very well. Do not, however, be tempted to send them up to clean your chimneys like Victorian urchins.

## GOOD AND BAD WAYS TO RESPOND IF THE KIDS ARE GOING COMPLETELY BERSERK

This is the ultimate test for any grandparent: suddenly the little darlings have gone from being the angels you know and love to devils incarnate (could it have been anything to do with the whopping bag full of E-numbers, er, sweets, you gave them earlier?). Anyway, you now have to deal with it, so what are the dos and don'ts?

| Do... | Don't... |
|---|---|
| Speak calmly, but firmly to explain that their behaviour is unacceptable. | Try to outscream them at the top of your voice as this will then become a competitive sport – and there can only be one winner, can't there? |
| Offer a small reward for good behaviour. | Make it another huge bag full of E-numbers! |
| Distract them with something like a glove puppet that will make them laugh. | Jump out from behind the curtains dressed in a full-body gorilla costume and scare the living daylights out of them. |

| Do... | Don't... |
|---|---|
| Use a quiet word and gentle methods to avoid unwanted behaviour. | Hand your grandchildren in to the police for a night in the cells just for leaving muddy footprints on the kitchen floor. |
| Stay calm and retain your composure. | Stay calm and retain your composure by drinking yourself senseless. |
| Try to keep your sense of humour. | Laugh in a manner that seems both hysterical and chilling. |
| Avoid accusing your grandchildren of being bad by using phrases such as: 'Why has a good person like you done something naughty like this?' | Try to improve their behaviour by calling in the services of a local exorcist. |

# THINGS THAT KIDS DO THAT ARE AN ABSOLUTE PAIN TO GRANDPARENTS

Children are very observant, and small children in particular are not yet masters of the art of diplomacy, so they will point out any physical flaw, blemish or oddity that they notice in you: 'Haven't you got big ears Granddad?' or 'Grandma, what are those funny little spots on the back of your hand?'

Children are also very forgetful about your physical capabilities these days. After challenging you to a race up the hill, they will be grimly fascinated as you gasp for breath and clutch your chest while reaching for your inhaler.

Children are often also still getting to grips with their own physical presence and its boundaries. Their elbows, for example, seem to have an in-built tracking device that homes in on any of your nick-nacks, particularly the most breakable ones, and sends them flying, only for you to go into a spectacular dive-catch that would not look out of place at a Lord's test match.

Young children also, of course, are wont to keep asking you questions ad infinitum like miniature TV quiz show presenters. Continual enquiries of 'Why?', 'How?' and 'But why?' will quickly cause you to leave the limits of your knowledge far behind and reduce you to a frothing wreck, lying on the floor silently mouthing 'Please stop asking me questions. I don't know anything'.

Your grandchildren will also probably have learnt more about food and nutrition in their few short years than anyone has ever bothered to tell you in your lifetime. They will therefore spend many hours lecturing you on why all the foodstuffs in your fridge and cupboards are extremely bad for your health and how if you hadn't spent the past few decades stuffing yourself with them you would still look like you were in your twenties.

Small children often also have the habit of befriending small creatures living around your house and giving names, for example, to various spiders they find. So heaven help you if you ever do any dusting or cleaning that might cause the little fellows to be evicted!

Your grandchildren will also regularly act like tiny prosecution lawyers who are able to remember everything you've done or said exactly, and who will give you chapter and verse on any occasions when you have told them things contrary to what you tell them now.

Needless to say, they will be much more expert than you at using any technological equipment you have in the house. This is useful sometimes, but at other times it may result in said equipment being reprogrammed in such a way that you can no longer get it to function at all.

They will also, of course, have much better eyesight than you, which they will again use to point out any imperfections about your house as though they were compiling a detailed hygiene report which could ultimately condemn your home as unfit for human habitation.

And if you ever tackle them for being rude because they spend all their time texting or playing on their tablets when you are trying to talk to them, they will demonstrate that they are in fact fully capable of multitasking and have followed everything you have said or done while they were composing and submitting their online report on the hygiene standards maintained in your home.

# FACTS DESIGNED TO STAGGER AND STUN KIDS

You really have to go to some lengths to stagger and stun a kid with facts these days. What with the telly, online videos, stuff going viral on the internet and some of the hair-raising 'facts' they learn from their friends in the playground ('Did you know you can die from a green spider bite?'), you may think they've heard it all, seen it all and possibly even done some of it. But there's always another fascinating fact just around the corner that is completely new to you – as you will remember from the last time you failed in a pub quiz.

Anything to do with big numbers is always awe-inspiring, even if they don't quite know the difference between a million, a billion and a trillion. Did you know a million seconds is 11½ days but a trillion seconds is nearly 32,000 years?!

Kids also like anything with a hint of danger or speed. Did you know a cheetah can run at 70 mph? So if you're being chased by a cheetah, Granddad's old car might not be quite fast enough to get away from him!

Anything slightly gory or scary is also an attention-grabber for kids. Over the course of your life you will produce enough saliva to fill two swimming pools – but please don't start now, or next time we go swimming!

Yes, that's something else that kids will find fascinating. Facts about their own bodies (my intestines are how long?!).

The unknown is also another constant source of wonder, whether it's ghosts, zombies or just plain old infinity. You know you've hit a winner when you hear them trying out these facts on someone else: if nothing's bigger than infinity what about infinity plus one?

And the great thing about all this is that you will have your mind boggled too! You will become a receptacle of knowledge unrivalled in your neighbourhood. You will know fascinating facts, staggering statistics, incredible information and googols of grossness. We can't guarantee, though, that there's still a hope in hell of you winning the pub quiz.

## HORRIFYING FACTS ABOUT THE DAYS WHEN GRANDDAD AND GRANDMA WERE SMALL CHILDREN

Now a lot of this will depend on how old you are, because some sneaky people get their grandparenting in early and make a start while they're still in their forties, or even thirties (the swines!). Others are a bit slow off the mark and don't finally become grandparents until they're in their seventies, which is probably enough to finish them off. The following, then, may have to be adapted here and there accordingly.

It will horrify most children to find that their grandparents did not have mobile phones when they were kids – it will be as shocking as learning that they did not have a right arm or a left leg. It will shock them even further if you are old enough not to have even had a landline in your house – and even if you did have a very early mobile phone, it will be hilarious for them to find that it was the same size as a packet of cream crackers.

In fact, every household gadget they take for granted may well have been missing from your childhood: the dishwasher, tumble dryer, central heating, microwave, freezer and, if you're really old, maybe even the fridge, washing machine and TV. Even if you had a TV as a kid it may have been only in black and white and have had two or three channels.

Everything else they take for granted and use every day was absent from your childhood: the internet, home computers, tablets, games consoles. My goodness, you were deprived!

And stuff they think is new is really old: vinyl records for example. Like flared trousers they have been in, out and back in again so frequently that you are totally confused as to whether you are at the height of fashion or a complete laughing stock.

And what about that central heating? You can probably remember the days before you had it when your bedroom was so freezing you could see your own breath in the air above the bed and you had to scrape ice off the windows.

There's a fair chance too that your mum and dad didn't have a car. 'So how did you get to the theme park?' 'We didn't have theme parks either!'

This will all be thoroughly shocking for the kids of today and they will either regard you with abject pity or a sneaking admiration that you managed to survive this long without the basic essentials of life, such as a selfie stick or a drone.

# FACTS ABOUT THE WORLD TODAY

You might think that with the internet available 24 hours a day, kids would know everything there is to know about everything – but they don't. They tend to only know about things that immediately interest them and/or will lead to gratification of some sort.

They will know the best shops to get their favourite sweets, the names, hobbies and interests of their favourite boy-band members, how to download apps to their phones and so on, but will they know that planet Earth is hurtling round the sun at 66,600 mph (the ultimate white-knuckle ride!) or that the crisp packet they drop in the park will still be around when they are grandparents? As it could take up to 80 years to decompose, it might even still be around when their grandchildren are grandparents!

A few more fab facts about the world:

- There are 195 countries in the world

- More than a quarter of those are in Africa

- One in five people in the world is Chinese

It's also fun to link up facts, so you could tell them that the deepest sea in the world is the Pacific Ocean (the world has seven seas and five oceans if you want to get picky) at 35,837 feet (as an oldie you're still allowed to use feet!). This means that if you accidentally dropped the highest mountain in the world, Everest (29,029 feet), in there, you'd have to dive down 1.29 miles before you reached the top of it!

Oh, and next time anyone moans about the weather being too hot you can threaten to take them to Death Valley in California, where the highest ever recorded temperature was 56.7°C (134.1°F) – that was in 1913; surely it should be even hotter now with global warming?

In the winter you can dismiss their complaints about the cold with the fab fact that they're lucky they're not in Antarctica, where the lowest recorded temperature was minus 89.2°C (–128.6°F). Brrrr!

And if they like snow, ask them how they'd feel about digging themselves out of a snowdrift 95 feet deep? That's about the height of six houses on top of each other! Luckily, that record wasn't set in the UK, but at Mount Baker in the USA. Hang on, isn't that the same country that had the highest ever temperature? Sounds like you've got to be prepared for anything if you go to the USA.

As a grandparent you always have to be ready to answer the most obscure questions, e.g. how long would it take to walk round the world? If you have a few facts up your sleeve and a handy calculator then you might be able to work it out for yourself, so here goes with a few more essential facts:

■ Circumference of Earth is 24,901 miles

■ Distance from Earth to the sun is 93,000,000 miles

■ Distance from Earth to the moon is 238,900 miles

■ Distance from surface to centre of Earth is 3,959 miles

So you can now work out that at an average walking speed of, say, 3 mph it would take 8,300 hours to walk round the earth, or 345 days, and you will be able to work out how long it would take to cycle, drive or skateboard round the earth.

Similarly, you can now work out how long it would take to walk to Australia through the centre of the earth (assuming you were wearing a very good heat-protection outfit). A mere 110 days since you ask! And that's as long as you don't sleep.

A few other facts you can use to juggle with and create your own fab facts:

■ The human population of the world is 7.6 billion

■ The surface area of Earth is 196.9 million square miles

■ The cat population of Earth is 600 million

■ The dog population of Earth is around 900 million (20 million of them are strays)

■ The ant population of Earth is estimated to be 10,000 trillion

So that means there are 12.5 people for every cat and about 1.5 cats for every dog! There are 38.5 people for every square mile on Earth – but only if quite a lot of them are living in the sea! And for every human on Earth there are around a million and a half ants, which will come as no surprise to anyone who has ever had a picnic on a nice sunny day.

So have fun working out your own fab facts.

# FACTS ABOUT HOUSEHOLD PETS

Cats and dogs bring many things to a home. These include funny smells, piles of fur, legions of fleas and the remains of unfortunate small creatures. They are, however, often a source of fascination for children. So when your pet pooch or moggy comes strolling through the house why not have an interesting fact or two about them ready to amaze and/or horrify your grandchildren?!

■ A cat is able to jump as much as five times its height and five or six times its body length. If a 6-foot-tall man could do that, he'd be able to jump the length of a bus!

■ Cats sleep between 16 and 20 hours a day. And some of them sleep even more than that. If a cat lives to be ten years old, that means they may have been asleep for eight years! It's a good job they do sleep that much because the rest of the time they're just pestering to be fed, leaving horrible smelly things in litter trays or flower beds and asking to have doors opened for them.

■ Cats spend around a third of their time (during the brief period they're awake) cleaning themselves.

■ A cat has 53 vertebrae in its back. Humans only have 34. That's why cats seem to extend like concertinas when you pick them up.

■ Cats are covered with approximately 130,000 hairs per square inch. That means that if you have a cat that weighs 4 kilograms, he/she will have 50,790,600 hairs. That's almost one hair for every single person living in England on one average-sized cat!

- Sir Isaac Newton is said to be the inventor of the cat flap. While Newton was doing his scientific experiments in a dark room his cat kept pushing the door open and spoiling everything. And so Newton came up with the idea of putting a little flap in the door!

- Grown-up cats only meow at humans, never at other cats. Kittens, however, meow to their mother.

- The world's richest cat was Blackie, who inherited £15 million from his owner.

- Dogs' nose prints are just as distinctive as human fingerprints – although you can usually identify when your dog has committed a crime in your house without the need for forensics!

- Dogs may have started living with humans over 15,000 years ago.

- All dogs are descended from wolves – even tiny Chihuahuas!

- Never feed chocolate to a dog – it contains a substance known as theobromine which is poisonous to them and might even kill them!

- Dogs walk round in a circle before lying down because if they were in the wild they would do this to flatten a patch of long grass into a bed.

- Dogs' main way of finding out about the world is through smell. While we humans have around 6 million smell receptors in our noses, dachshunds have 125 million and German shepherds have 220 million. And despite this they spend most of their time sniffing other dogs' bottoms.

- And it is through smelling each other's bottoms that dogs learn about each other. The smell can tell them how old the other dog is, how fit they are and what they've had for dinner!

- While dogs have a much better sense of smell than humans, they only have about one-sixth the number of taste buds we have.

- Great Danes usually stand around 28 to 30 inches tall; Chihuahuas are between 6 and 9 inches tall.

- Dogs cannot see as well as people; they are sometimes described as being colour blind. What they see is a bit like what we might see when it's beginning to get dark in the evening.

- According to Guinness World Records, the heaviest cat ever recorded was Himmy who lived in Australia and weighed nearly 47 pounds (21 kilograms). That's about the same as three or four bowling balls. Or indeed five normal-sized cats.

# FACTS ABOUT INSECTS AND CREEPY-CRAWLIES

Careful with these ones! It's probably best not to use them if they might traumatise any grandchildren who have a phobia about insects or spiders. Reserve these instead for your grandchildren who have a morbid obsession with the habits of creepy-crawlies!

- There are estimated to be 10 quintillion (10,000,000,000,000,000,000) insects alive at any one time on Earth. That's 10 million million million. Or around 1.3 billion insects for every single person.

- The largest insects to have ever lived on Earth were griffinflies which had wingspans up to 28 inches. Luckily they died out more than 250 million years ago.

- One of the longest insects around today is Chan's megastick, a stick insect found in Borneo which can be nearly 2 feet long.

- The mosquito is the deadliest creature on Earth. It kills over 1 million people a year and may have killed half the people who have ever lived. But luckily mosquitoes in the UK do not cause much more bother than the occasional itchy bite!

- The spider with the biggest leg span is probably the giant huntsman spider which is found in Laos. Its legs can span up to 1 foot.

- The Goliath birdeater spider found in rainforests in South America has a leg span of up to 11 inches but it is otherwise bulkier and heavier than the giant huntsman and has fangs up to 1 inch long. Despite its name, it is more likely to eat worms than birds.

■ The *Patu marplesi* which has a body length of only 0.01 inches (0.3 mm) may be the world's smallest spider. You could fit ten of them on the end of a pencil.

■ Female spiders can lay up to 3,000 eggs at a time. The eggs hatch into spiderlings.

■ Spiders' blood is blue not red. This is because they have copper in their blood rather than iron like we do.

■ Spiders do not have any teeth (although, as we just mentioned, they do have fangs) and have to pump their digestive juices into food so they can suck their dinner back in as a liquid. Spiders are effectively therefore on an all-soup diet.

■ To make one pound of honey (that's one large jar), a bee would have to visit 2 million flowers. And of course no single bee could do this. One teaspoon of honey is the entire life's work of 12 bees.

# FACTS ABOUT FOOD

Sometimes those of us in later life become obsessed with the things we eat. This happens either in the pursuit of excellent cuisine or to avoid unhealthy or fattening foods, or just because we can't find anything else to read at breakfast time and end up reading everything printed on the side of the cornflakes box.

Your grandchildren may be less fascinated if you choose to lecture them on every single one of the E-numbers in their favourite foods. Instead here's a selection of random facts about food which can be served as a side order with the grandchildren's dinner or while wandering around the supermarket aisles!

- On average, human beings eat about 1.8 kilograms of food a day. If you lived to be 80 that would add up to 52,596 kilograms in total. And in grandparents' imperial units, that's nearly 52 tons!

- Humans spend about five years of their lives eating.

- They also spend one and a half years of their lives on the toilet!

- Carrots all used to be purple, but were cultivated by Dutch farmers in the seventeenth century to be orange.

- And if you eat too many carrots, they might start to turn you orange (but you'd have to eat quite a lot).

- Honey will never go off or go bad. Neither will salt or sugar (as long as it's kept in a clean, dry airtight container).

Water won't really go off either. But it will absorb some nasty things if it's left exposed to air for too long. The expiry date on bottles of water therefore isn't really the expiry date of the water but of the plastic bottle the water is in!

■ Most of the bananas we eat are genetic clones of the Cavendish banana. It was produced not to have seeds which means it has to be cloned instead.

■ Strawberries aren't actually berries. Bananas, however, are officially berries!

■ If you eat lots of beetroot it will turn your wee pink.

■ Cucumbers are 96 per cent water.

■ Even a potato is 80 per cent water (which you could say is not that much more than a young grandchild, at around 65 per cent water!).

■ Cutting up an onion releases a gas that will make your eyes water, but you can make it go away by running a hot water tap and possibly rinsing your fingers as well.

■ Ripe cranberries can be bounced like a ball. If you try doing this and discover that they're overripe, however, you will end up with a horrible splodgy mess on the floor!

■ Brussels sprouts, broccoli, cabbage and cauliflower all belong to the same family of plants.

■ The Maya people in Mesoamerica used to use cocoa beans as money.

■ For the first few hundred years that chocolate was known in Europe, it was used as a drink. Eating chocolate was first developed by Fry's in 1847 and the first milk chocolate appeared in 1875.

■ A sort of ice cream was invented over 2,000 years ago in China using a mix of rice, milk and snow.

# FACTS ABOUT SPACE

Life, the universe and everything should fascinate your grandchildren. If not, there's nothing much else to choose from! Who knows if your grandchildren will grow up to be the next Professor Brian Cox, but it's probably best not to make up your answers when they ask you about space, stars and planets. You may, however, find it a bit difficult to give them an accurate, detailed lecture on cosmology, but perhaps a few exciting facts will give the little ones some cause to wonder and might even inspire them to learn more for themselves.

- **The sun is so big you could fit over a million Earths inside it.**

- The sun's mass makes up 99.8 per cent of all the mass in our solar system.

- **The nearest star to Earth (apart from the sun) is Proxima Centauri but it's still 4.24 light years away. If you travelled there in a space rocket it would take 73,000 years.**

- A light year is the distance that light travels in a single year. Light travels 186,282 miles per second (299,792 kilometres per second) which is even faster than Usain Bolt. So that's about 5.879 trillion miles a year (5,878,612,843,200 miles; 9,460,710,307,526.861 kilometres).

- **The Milky Way galaxy is about 100,000 light years across. So that would take 1.7 billion (1,721,698,113) years to cross (if you used the same rocket you just used to go to Proxima Centauri).**

- In the centre of the Milky Way is believed to be a black hole which is as heavy as 3 million suns.

■ It took the *Voyager* spacecraft about 12.5 years just to reach Pluto from Earth.

■ There are believed to be 100 billion galaxies in the observable universe.

■ There are more stars in the universe than there are grains of sand on all the beaches on Earth.

■ The universe is thought to be 13.8 billion years old.

■ Our solar system formed about 4.6 billion years ago. So it's only existed for a third of the time since the Big Bang.

■ If you were given a teaspoon of coal at the moment of the Big Bang and had constantly been removing one atom from it every second ever since for the past 13.8 billion years, you would by today have only got through about 7.26 per cent of it (so 92.74 per cent would still be left!). That gives you an idea of just how many atoms there are in a teaspoon of coal (aka a small lump of carbon)!

■ If you went into space your spine would straighten out because of the lack of gravity. You could maybe become 5 centimetres (2 inches) taller in space (and it might fix Granddad's bad back).

■ You only weigh what you weigh because of the size of the earth and the gravitational pull that a planet this size creates. Someone who weighs 68 kilograms on Earth would weigh 159 kilograms on Jupiter (which is much bigger than Earth) but only 4 kilograms on Mars (which is almost half the size of Earth). Not that anyone could stand on Jupiter because it's a gas planet and so doesn't have a rocky surface!

■ 68 per cent of the universe is made up of dark energy and 27 per cent is dark matter (the nature of both remains uncertain). All normal matter (in other words, all the sorts of things that humans have ever been able to observe) makes up less than 5 per cent of the universe.

- No matter how old you yourself are, all the matter that makes up your body is billions of years old.

- At the moment of the Big Bang all the matter that is now in the universe existed in one tiny point.

- Hydrogen and helium make up most of the visible matter in the universe.

- Heavier elements were formed by the immense gravitational pressure on individual atoms inside stars. So the elements that form your body were made inside stars.

- If you travel upwards it's only about 100 kilometres (62 miles) until you leave Earth's atmosphere. If you could drive into space it would only take about an hour to get there (presuming the traffic wasn't too bad).

# FACTS ABOUT HUMAN BEINGS

There are of course endless extraordinary facts about human beings and our bodies. But do go easy with some of the more icky facts, and again make sure not to use them to traumatise the more sensitive of your grandchildren!

◼ Sneezes have been said to travel at 100 miles per hour from people's noses. The normal speed may, however, be a third of this – but that's still pretty fast. And one sneeze can spread 100,000 germs into the air.

◼ **Your nails grow 1 centimetre every 100 days. So if you never cut your nails and lived to be 80 they would end up 3 metres long.**

◼ An adult human heart is about the same size as the same person's fist and weighs between 220 to 260 grams – so only about 8 or 9 ounces. If a person lives to be 80 their heart will have beaten over 3 billion times. And that's probably without stopping for a rest.

◼ A pair of human feet have 250,000 sweat glands between them and are capable of producing about half a pint of sweat every day.

◼ Your bones are five times stronger than steel of equivalent thickness. However, they are considerably more brittle – so don't try hitting them with a hammer to see whether your bones or the hammer last longer.

◼ **You have around 270 bones in your body when you're born but only 206 when you've grown up (because some of them fuse together as you age).**

◼ Your hands and feet contain almost half of the total bones in all your body.

- From the moment you're born your eyes stay the same size, but your nose and ears will keep getting bigger through your life!

- The cells in your body are constantly renewing themselves. Even your skeleton completely regenerates itself over about ten years. So if you live to be 80, you will have had about eight skeletons!

- Your outer skin flakes off and regrows every 27 days.

- A human sheds about 1.6 pounds (0.72 kilograms) of skin in a year. If you live to be 80 you may have shed 58 kilograms of skin. That's about the same weight as an entire person!

- The total length of all the blood vessels in the human body is about 60,000 miles or 97,000 kilometres. That's getting on for 2½ times the distance round the equator.

- There are about 1,000 types of bacteria on your skin. Lots of them are harmless and lots are useful!

- There may be between 25 million to 500 million bacteria per square inch on your body.

- You have probably got more bacteria in your mouth than there are people in the world. So don't forget to brush your teeth!

- Your hair grows about 0.5 inches or 1.25 centimetres a month. That's about 6 inches a year. So if a 6-foot-tall person wanted to grow their hair all the way down to their feet it would take 12 years! So if Granddad is so old why does he have so little hair?

- You have enough iron in your body to make an iron nail. Possibly two or three!

- Ninety-nine per cent of the human body is made up of six chemical elements – oxygen, carbon, hydrogen, nitrogen, calcium and phosphorus. There are another five elements which are also essential for life contained in the remaining 1 per cent – potassium, sulphur, sodium, chlorine and magnesium.

- A lot of a human body is water. An adult man's body is 60 per cent water. A newborn baby is 73 per cent water.

- Human DNA is about 50 per cent the same as the DNA of a banana.

- Human DNA is about 96 per cent the same as the DNA of a chimpanzee.

- And your DNA is about 99.9 per cent the same as any other human being.

# FACTS ABOUT DINOSAURS

Children are often fascinated by dinosaurs, those great, grey, slow-moving creatures that plodded around Earth millions of years ago. Obviously, your grandkids must think that dinosaurs and their grandparents have much in common and may possibly be one and the same species. Nevertheless, here are a few fascinating dinosaur facts which you can use to try and impress them about the creatures that roamed Earth millions of years ago (around the time you started school!).

- Dinosaurs lived on Earth from about 230 million years ago to about 65 million years ago. So that's about 165 million years.

- Earth itself is 4.54 billion years old (4,543,000,000 years).

- There is then a 65-million-year gap between the dinosaurs dying out and the first humans appearing.

- Humans (or technically our human-like ancestors) only first began to appear about 2 million years ago, compared to the 165 million years that the dinosaurs existed on Earth.

- Seven hundred different types of dinosaur have so far been identified and named. And they were around for so long there must have been loads more.

- Dinosaurs therefore existed for about 82.5 times as long as the total time that people have existed.

- There were over 65 million years between Tyrannosaurus rex dying out and the first humans appearing, but the gap between dinosaurs like

Diplodocus and Stegosaurus dying out and Tyrannosaurus rex first appearing is believed to be around 80 million years, or possibly even longer.

■ William Buckland was the first person to study and name a dinosaur fossil. He called it *Megalosaurus* in 1824.

■ One of the biggest, heaviest dinosaurs is believed to have been *Argentinosaurus huinculensis* which lived about 95 million years ago and may have measured as much as 39.7 metres (130 feet) from the tip of its nose to the end of its tail. That's four and a half buses or two fifths of a football pitch.

■ *Argentinosaurus huinculensis* is believed to have weighed 96.4 metric tons. That's about the same as 14 elephants or 55 cars.

■ And like most other dinosaurs *Argentinosaurus huinculensis* was a vegetarian.

■ But that's not the biggest creature that's ever lived. It's the blue whale, which is bigger than any dinosaur.

■ Some of the biggest vegetarian dinosaurs may have had to eat a ton of food every day. That's like eating a pile of vegetables the size of a bus.

■ But in fact most dinosaurs weren't massive at all. Usually dinosaurs were human-sized or even smaller.

■ Giant dinosaurs however had giant fleas five or ten times the size of modern-day fleas who were armed with long, serrated tube-like syringe needles to pierce through the dinosaur skin and suck their blood.

■ Dinosaurs are believed to have been wiped out when an asteroid hit Earth 65 million years ago. There is a 110-mile-wide (180-kilometre-wide) crater in Yucatan, Mexico which is thought to have been caused by the impact.

There are also believed to have been a massive number of volcanic explosions around the same time in history. So those may not have helped either!

But dinosaurs may not officially be extinct after all. A lot of scientists believe that the birds we see today have evolved from dinosaurs and should be classified as the same sorts of creatures.

# THINGS THAT GRANDPARENTS DO THAT ARE AN ABSOLUTE PAIN TO KIDS

Remember when your kids were teenagers and everything you did or said seemed to annoy or embarrass them? Then they grew up and learnt to be just as annoying as you, so when their kids are teenagers they'll understand what you went through.

In the meantime, you have it within your power to be quite irritating to your grandchildren without any aid from the parents. For a start, being old is quite annoying. You will not be able to keep up those shoulder carries quite as long as Daddy. You will be hypersensitive to noise, which is a bit unfortunate as that is one thing grandchildren excel in making. And by some strange quirk of evolution, at the same time as being hypersensitive to noise you might also be a bit hard of hearing so might need things repeated two or three times – 'You want what? Eh? No, you'll have to speak up, dear. What is it you want? Oh, you want me to stop the car because you need the loo? What's that dear? Oh, it's too late, is it?'

Other things that grandchildren will find annoying include:

- Grandma spitting on her hanky and wiping something mucky off a grandchild's face.

- Giving them big slobbery kisses when they're going home.

- Testing them on their times tables.

- Giving them boiled sweets instead of proper kids' sweets.

- Asking young teenagers if they've got a boyfriend or girlfriend yet.

- Asking them what is 'top of the pops' at the moment.

- Pretending to like it.

- Saying 'Haven't you grown?!'

- Asking funny questions like 'Has the cat got your tongue?'

- Hearing Granddad or Grandma's stories about the old days for the umpteenth time.

- Being told how much they look like their mother, father or some other hideous old relative.

- Having Granddad or Grandma absent-mindedly call them by their mother or father's name.

- Being promised a treat for dinner only to find it's something that people would only have considered a treat during wartime rationing.

- The use of phrases that no one else uses these days, such as 'snaps' for photos, 'the flicks' for the cinema and 'bobby-dazzler' as an epithet of great excellence or attractiveness.

- Granddad or Grandma's presumption that the grandchildren will be able to remember events from decades before they were born.

- The use of cutlery and crockery covered in stains which have been there since before they were born.

- Granddad and Grandma's constant detailing of health problems that run in the family and which they can look forward to getting in the future.

- Coming to school concerts and plays, falling asleep and snoring loudly.

# SUMMING UP

So, we hope this little book has given you a few ideas about how to keep the grandchildren amused when they come round, or even when you're out and about with them.

We also hope that, secretly, you have had as much fun as the grandchildren have, because really, that's what it's all about, isn't it? Suddenly you have been given free licence to enjoy things you haven't done for years. When your kids were younger you had a second go at all those things you enjoyed as a kid, building sandcastles, making daisy chains, going on the roundabout in the playground, kicking a football around, then suddenly your kids grew out of it. You didn't, of course. If you'd had your way you would have carried on forever, going to funfairs, eating candyfloss, playing conkers, whirling sparklers around in the dark to make fiery rings in the air, but it was all snatched away from you when your kids suddenly wanted to ride motorbikes, wear make-up and go clubbing.

Well, this is your third chance. People talk about a second childhood, but if your kids keep turning out grandchildren who knows, you might have a fourth, fifth or sixth childhood to look forward to as well. Curled up on the sofa reading fairy stories or watching kids' TV and scoffing sweets – what's not to like?

And the great thing is that each generation of kids brings with it a whole new lot of fantastic toys, gadgets, gimmicks, jokes, children's stories, films and so on, and you've still got all the old favourites to introduce them to. Play your cards right and they can enjoy the time of their lives – and so can you!

GRANDPARENTING
FOR BEGINNERS

Clive Whichelow

£6.99

Hardback

ISBN: 978-1-84953-753-7

*Just when you thought your kids were off your hands...*

... along come the grandchildren. The world has changed since you had little ones of your own – you may now have to read bedtime stories from an e-book, buy designer babygrows and check all their sweets for E-numbers... Welcome to grandparenting twenty-first-century style!

SO YOU'RE A GRANDPARENT

Mike Haskins and
Clive Whichelow

£6.99

Hardback

ISBN: 978-1-78685-047-8

It's the best of times and the worst of times. You're welcoming a new addition to the family, but you're now officially old. You're also an eternal babysitter. On the plus side, you can enjoy spoiling the little darlings rotten and hand them back at the end of the day before the nappies start overflowing.

PARENTING FOR BEGINNERS

Clive Whichelow

£6.99

Hardback

ISBN: 978-1-84953-836-7

*There's a baby on its way... help!*

How hard can parenting be, really? We've all seen it done before. But parenthood involves answering some very tricky questions, such as: should the father be there at the birth – especially if he can barely remember being there at the conception? And how long before the mother can start drinking wine again?

HOW TO SURVIVE RETIREMENT

Mike Haskins and
Clive Whichelow

£6.99

Hardback

ISBN: 978-1-78685-049-2

Freedom at last! But there's an awfully long time between cornflakes and cocoa, and a limit to how many sudokus you can do. You need survival skills:

FINANCIAL WIZARDRY: how to get three cups of tea out of one bag.

SPARKLING CONVERSATION: 300 different ways to discuss the weather.

This mischievous little book will help you enjoy your golden years with tongue-in-cheek advice and cheeky illustrations.

If you're interested in finding out more about our books, find us on Facebook at **Summersdale Publishers** and follow us on Twitter at **@Summersdale**.

**www.summersdale.com**